An Introduction to Chemical Systems in the Laboratory

Caroline Cvetkovic

■ **Fall 2007**

University of Illinois at Urbana-Champaign

Don DeCoste
Lauren Denofrio
Jesse Miller

HAYDEN
HM
McNEIL

ISBN 978-0-7380-2397-7

Hayden-McNeil Publishing, Inc.
14903 Pilot Drive
Plymouth, MI 48170
www.hmpublishing.com

Denofrio 2397-7 F07

Introduction to Chemistry 103

Experiments in the Laboratory

Appendices

Lab Report Evaluation Forms

General Information

Name: _____

Campus Address: _____

Telephone Number: _____

E-mail: _____

LABORATORY SECTION INFORMATION

Section Number: _____

Time: _____

Room: _____

TA's Name: _____

TA's Office Hours: _____

TA's Office Number: _____

DISCUSSION SECTION INFORMATION

Section Number: _____

Time: _____

Room: _____

TA's Name: _____

TA's Office Hours: _____

TA's Office Number: _____

INTRODUCTION TO CHEMISTRY 103

Introduction to Chemistry 103

Preface

Welcome to Chemistry 103! This semester you will experience an introduction to the chemistry laboratory at the college level. You will complete six unique chemistry experiments in the laboratory. These are designed to help you better understand the chemistry you are learning or have learned in Chemistry 102 or a similar course. In addition, you will complete numerous virtual experiments via computer that utilize digital photography and video. These "interactive video lessons" will help you learn by experimenting even when you cannot be in the laboratory setting.

Many of the theories you will learn about as you take chemistry here at the University of Illinois have been developed because of the efforts of research scientists in the laboratory. Laboratory practice is a huge component of chemistry, and represents the only avenue for investigating chemical quandaries that cannot be "solved" with the naked eye. You will do some deducing of your own this semester, as you determine the identity, composition, or qualities of several systems or chemicals.

This manual is designed to help you on your way in Chemistry 103. Its aim is to guide you through the experiments you will undertake and help introduce you to several topics, techniques, and principles of chemistry. The experiments described within these pages are intended to introduce you to laboratory work, but not to train you to be a professional chemist. It is important to us that this course and the experiments in it be enjoyable for you, not overwhelming, boring, or worst of all—both! It is our hope that you will find these laboratory exercises challenging, interesting, and exciting!

Finally, Chemistry 103 is for many people their very first laboratory course. Although the course is made for the first-time laboratory student, you may be apprehensive or have questions. The teaching staff and course director welcome your concerns and questions, whenever they arise throughout the semester. Feel free to e-mail, visit during office hours, or ask your laboratory instructor if you need help with techniques or materials.

Again, welcome to Chemistry 103!

Chemistry 103 Course Policies

You must read this section before coming to your first scheduled laboratory period!

■ REQUIRED COMPONENTS OF THE COURSE

1. Laboratory Previews

Each of the six experiments for this course is preceded by a **"Laboratory Preview"** assignment, which can be found online. It is a 10–12 question quiz taken on the computer. It must be **completed by 8:00 a.m. on the day of the corresponding experiment**. The preview will correct your answers for you and present you with your score after each attempt. Before the deadline, multiple attempts are allowed. The "Lab Preview" will not be accepted late. It is recommended that these assignments be started as early as possible, as last minute computer problems will not be considered grounds for an extension on the assignment. It is recommended that you complete these quizzes at the Chemistry Learning Center.

2. Laboratory Experiments

There are **six laboratory experiments** in this course. You will **complete each experiment according to the schedule for your section**. To find this schedule, go to Chemistry 103 online and click on "Scheduling." Click on the link for your section number. Your section number can be found on your class schedule.

You should come to your laboratory section having completed the online Lab Preview quiz and having prepared your laboratory notebook for data recording and analysis. See page xiv for more information on preparing your laboratory notebook.

You are not excused from the laboratory unless the reason for missing an experiment falls under one of the categories described in the *Attendance for the Course* section, on page xiii. If you are excused from a laboratory experiment, you must still complete both the Lab Preview and the Post-Laboratory Quiz Multiple Choice section.

3. Post-Laboratory Quizzes

After completing an experiment, you will have one week to complete two **Post-Laboratory Quizzes** pertaining to the experiment. These quizzes can be found on Chemistry 103 online, under the "Lon Capa quizzes" link. The multiple choice (MC) quiz consists of 5–10 objective questions and the free response (FR) quiz consists of 5–10 free response questions, all taken on the computer. Both must be **completed by 5:00 p.m. exactly one week from the day you performed the experiment**. Before the deadline, multiple attempts are allowed. Your Post-Lab quizzes will not be scored until the following week. The Post-Lab quizzes will not be accepted late. Again, last-minute computer problems are not grounds for an extension. It is recommended that you take the MC Post-Lab quizzes at the Chemistry Learning Center. For FR Post-Lab quizzes, past students found it useful to answer the essay questions using a word processing program (like Microsoft Word) and then copy and paste them into the quiz. This way, students can save their work.

4. Interactive Video Laboratories

Throughout the semester, you will complete Interactive Video Labs (IVLs) on the computers in the Chemistry Learning Center (CLC) in Room 212 Chemistry Annex. **There are six sets of IVLs to be completed in this course**. The due dates for these IVLs depend on your section. See your section schedule on Chemistry 103 online to find your section's due dates for each of the six sets of IVLs. More information can be found on page xxiii of this manual.

■ ACCESSING CHEMISTRY 103 ONLINE

Go to: *www.chem.uiuc.edu*

Choose: "Course Web Sites"

Choose: "Chemistry 103"

It is extremely important that you log on to the "Lon Capa Quizzes" link for Chemistry 103 prior to your first laboratory period. On the Chem 103 website, you will find five very important links.

1. The **"Scheduling"** link provides you with a semester-long schedule for each section. Find your section's schedule and PRINT IT OUT! This is the ONLY WAY you will know when your section meets and when your IVLs are due.

2. The **"Lon Capa Quizzes"** link will allow you to access each Preview assignment and each Post-Lab assignment. Clicking on this link will bring you to the Login page for Lon Capa. Enter your NetID as your login and enter your password. Your password is your Active Directory Password.

Follow the log-in directions on www. chem.uiuc.edu for help logging in. E-mail the Instructional Technology staff for help (e-mail is posted on www.chem.uiuc.edu).

3. The **"Contact Information and Office Hours"** link provides all of the Chemistry 103 staff information. Using this link, you can find the information to contact your course director and teaching assistants.

4. The **"Experiments: Online Laboratory Syllabi"** link contains useful preparatory information for the lab. For each experiment, it provides a detailed procedure with color photographs of each step in the experiment. It also provides review questions to help you prepare for your Lab Preview quiz. It is a good idea to print out the procedure containing color photographs and bring this with you to the lab.

5. The **"Gradebook"** link provides you with the scores on all of your Chemistry 103 assignments.

■ REQUIRED MATERIALS FOR THE COURSE

You are required to purchase the following for Chemistry 103:

1. Lab coat or apron

A lab coat or apron can be purchased at any of the campus bookstores.

2. Goggles

All students, teaching assistants, instructors and visitors in the laboratory must wear regulation safety goggles as required by STATE LAW. You must wear goggles at all times in the laboratory or you will be asked to leave immediately. If you must be reminded to wear goggles in the laboratory, your TA will deduct points from your laboratory grade.

A pair of goggles can be purchased at any of the campus bookstores.

It is strongly advised that you do not wear contacts while in the laboratory. They readily adsorb vapors from solvents that are detrimental to the eye. Safety goggles are not "air tight" and therefore do not completely eliminate this adsorption. If you choose to wear contacts in the laboratory, you must wear an "I wear contacts" sticker on your lab coat or apron. Your TA can provide you with this sticker.

3. Breakage Fee Card

You must purchase a Laboratory Breakage Fee Card from the Illini Union Bookstore. Your TA will collect this card during the first laboratory period when you are completing your Check-In. You will not be able to continue working in the lab for the second laboratory period unless your TA has received your breakage fee card.

4. Chemistry 103 Laboratory Manual "General Chemistry Experiments"

You cannot use an old version of this manual this semester, as the course has been redesigned to include new experiments and policies. You must purchase the current version of the manual.

5. Bound, spiral laboratory notebook with perforated carbon pages

See the section entitled *The Laboratory Notebook*, on the following pages for more details.

■ ATTENDANCE FOR THE COURSE

Students are required to attend all laboratory periods. You must attend the section in which you are enrolled. Come to class 2–5 minutes early. If you miss opening lecture by your TA, 2 points will be deducted; 5 points if you come 10 minutes late. All absences will be considered unexcused except in the following cases. Excuses MUST be submitted in a timely manner.

1. **Medical excuse.** You must provide a signed doctor's note from a physician or from McKinley Health Center to your TA. You will be excused from the laboratory report and the Post-Lab FR quiz. You are responsible for making up both the Lab Preview and the Post-Lab MC quizzes.

2. **Family emergency**. In the case that you cannot attend class because you must leave campus for an unexpected emergency, you must provide documentation from the Emergency Dean to your TA. You will be excused from the laboratory report and the Post-Lab FR quiz. You are responsible for making up both the Lab Preview and the Post-Lab MC quizzes.

3. **Participation in a University-sponsored activity**. An example of such an activity is participation in the Marching Illini or a University sports team. Intramurals, student-sponsored clubs and activities, or registered student organization events are not considered University-sponsored and thus do not excuse you from class. You must provide documentation regarding your absence to your TA in order to be excused in the case of a University-sponsored activity. This documentation is required one week prior to your absence. You are responsible for making up both the Lab Preview and the Post-Lab MC quizzes, but will be excused from the laboratory report and Post-Lab FR quiz.

In the case of any absence, we ask that you try to inform your TA or the course director prior to missing class. A maximum of one excused absence will be accepted.

Unexcused absences will result in a grade of ZERO for the laboratory report and the Post-Lab FR quiz. Students arriving late for lab will have points deducted from the laboratory report grade.

Any student who misses more than 2 laboratory periods during the semester will automatically fail the course.

■ GRADING FOR THE COURSE
Please note: Chemistry 103 follows the University plus/minus system for grading

> The grading for this course will be as follows:
>
> 6 Laboratory Previews (10 points each)..............................60 pts
>
> 6 Laboratory Reports (30–50 points each) ....200 pts
>
> 5 Post-Lab MC Quizzes (10 points each)...........................50 pts
>
> 5 Post-Lab FR Quizzes (10 points each) ....50 pts
>
> 6 Interactive Video Lesson Sets (2 points per IVL) ....70 pts
>
> **Total** ....430 pts

The course is not curved (i.e., 70–73% is a C–, 74–76% is a C, 77–79% is a C+, 80–83% is a B–, 84–86% is a B, 87–89% is a B+, 90–93% is a A–, and 94–100% is an A). However, lab report grades for each section will be normalized across the class average and verified with the computer-graded portions of the course. This will eliminate discrepancies between sections due to the differing grading styles of each TA.

■ OTHER IMPORTANT COURSE INFORMATION ITEMS

1. Drawer assignments

You and a partner will be assigned a laboratory drawer containing glassware and equipment for each experiment. You are responsible for the contents of this drawer while it is assigned to you. Lab equipment should be kept clean. After each laboratory period, all glassware should be washed and dried. All broken equipment should be reported to the TA, who will then have the laboratory manager deduct the cost from your breakage fee card. Each time you leave the laboratory, you must quickly inventory the contents of the drawer to be sure that nothing has been left on the benchtop.

2. Medical insurance

Each student at the University is responsible for providing his/her own medical insurance coverage. If a student is injured or becomes ill during laboratory, costs of transportation and treatment are the responsibility of the student. Check to be sure that your insurance coverage is adequate.

3. Contact information

If you have any questions or concerns throughout the semester, you should contact the Course Director. Their contact information is included online.

■ THE LABORATORY NOTEBOOK

In the laboratory notebook you purchase for this class, you will keep a record of each experiment you complete. At the end of each laboratory period, you will submit the original record to your TA as your laboratory report and keep the carbon copies of these pages in your notebook for your records.

Use the notebook required for Chemistry 103. In general, a laboratory notebook is bound with spiral binding so that pages cannot be removed. Notebooks with alternating perforated pages for use with carbon paper are appropriate, since one page is permanent and the other may be handed in. You will make a carbon copy of all lab reports. The original will be turned in for grading, while the carbon copy will remain bound in the notebook as a record of your work.

Record data and observations in ink. No pencil writing is accepted. Notes extraneous to data (puzzling observations, questions about procedure or results, etc.) should also be recorded.

The record of each experiment should be in a format that allows convenient organization of pertinent data and observations. Carefully read the entire experiment before coming to lab. This will help you visualize the purpose and procedure and organize your work. The report of each week's experiment should begin at the top of a new page, following the format below:

I. Title, date experiment is performed.

Include the title of your experiment at the top of the first page along with your full name and the date. This should be done before coming to lab, as part of your pre-laboratory preparation.

II. Introduction.

In three or four sentences of your own words give the purpose of the experiment and the principles upon which it is based. State as well the techniques or chemical principles that are going to be part of the experiment. This should be done before coming to lab, as part of your pre-laboratory preparation.

III. Procedure.

This MUST be done before lab. Make a brief outline of the steps you will follow in the experiment, **and be sure to include all the pertinent safety considerations**. The outline can be a combination of phrases, sentences, symbols, and chemical equations. Write the outline in your own words. The goal of this section is to write clearly enough that you could do the experiment using only this procedure and not having to use your lab manual at all. You may use an outline form that numbers the steps if this helps to organize the information. You should include the chemical equations taking place at each step. This should be done before coming to lab, as part of the pre-laboratory preparation.

IV. Observations and Data.

Record all data and observations neatly in logical order with appropriate labels and with the proper number of significant figures. Pre-made tables will help you do this efficiently and neatly. Also, include all of your observations during the experiment. It is important to be very thorough and record the color of solutions, any changes you witness in the system during an experiment, the time it took to complete a step of the experiment, the type of glassware or equipment used, etc. Your goal is to write enough information that someone could reproduce your experiment just by looking at your lab report. You should create the data tables before coming to the lab, as part of your pre-laboratory preparation. You will fill in these tables and note your observations while you are in the laboratory.

V. Analysis.

Answer the questions found throughout the experiment. Show calculations neatly, being careful to use the proper number of significant figures and units when reporting your results. Note any confusion or revelation you experience while doing the experiment. Include answers to the calculations questions at the end of each experiment. For all calculations, show all your work and be very neat so that your TA can find your answers. Conclude this section with some remarks regarding the results obtained; three to four sentences will suffice, but do not feel limited if you need to include additional information. You will complete this section of the report while in the laboratory.

■ **EXAMPLE LAB REPORT:**

Look over the following example lab report for more help in writing lab reports.

Name: Lisa Smith   **Date:** 05/26/05

Experiment: Determining the Identity of an Unknown Acid

Introduction: The purpose of this experiment is to determine the identity of an unknown acid by manual titration of acid samples with a standardized solution of the strong base, NaOH. At the endpoint of a titration, when the indicator changes color slightly, the moles of base added via a burette are equal to the moles of acid in the original sample. First, a dilute solution of NaOH will be standardized by manual titration employing standardized HCl. This standardized NaOH will be used to manually titrate samples of the unknown acid, thus identifying the number of moles of acid in the samples. Since the original number of moles of acid and grams of acid are known, the molar mass of the unknown acid can be found using the equation Molar Mass = grams ÷ moles. Thus the acid can be identified by its molar mass.

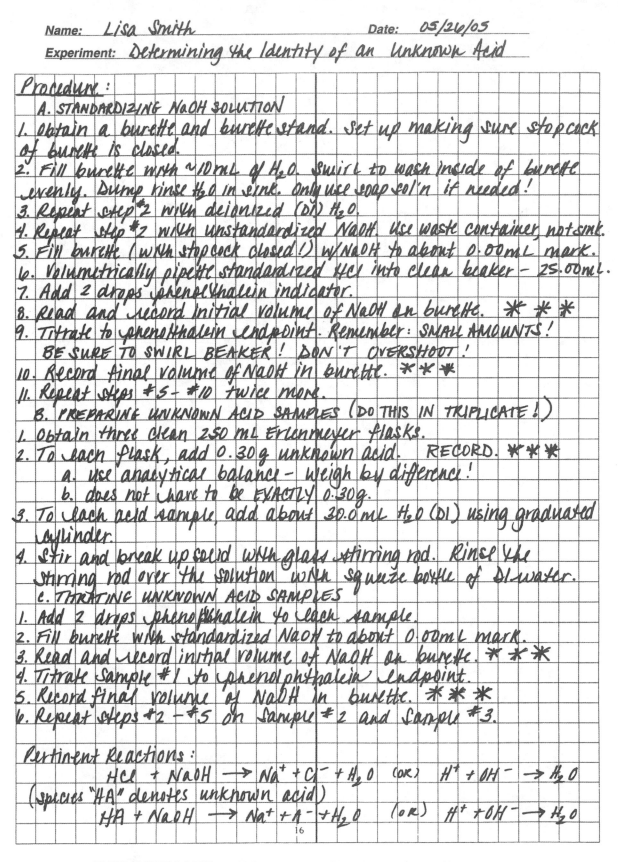

Name: Lisa Smith   Date: 05/26/05

Experiment: Determining the Identity of an Unknown Acid

Procedure:
   A. STANDARDIZING NaOH SOLUTION
1. Obtain a burette and burette stand. Set up making sure stopcock of burette is closed.
2. Fill burette with ~10mL of H_2O. Swirl to wash inside of burette evenly. Dump rinse H_2O in sink. Only use soap sol'n if needed!
3. Repeat step #2 with deionized (DI) H_2O.
4. Repeat step #2 with unstandardized NaOH. Use waste container, not sink.
5. Fill burette (with stopcock closed!) w/NaOH to about 0.00mL mark.
6. Volumetrically pipette standardized HCl into clean beaker — 25.00mL.
7. Add 2 drops phenolphthalein indicator.
8. Read and record initial volume of NaOH on burette. ✳✳✳
9. Titrate to phenolphthalein endpoint. Remember: SMALL AMOUNTS!
   BE SURE TO SWIRL BEAKER! DON'T OVERSHOOT!
10. Record final volume of NaOH in burette. ✳✳✳
11. Repeat steps #5 - #10 twice more.
   B. PREPARING UNKNOWN ACID SAMPLES (DO THIS IN TRIPLICATE!)
1. Obtain three clean 250 mL Erlenmeyer flasks.
2. To each flask, add 0.30g unknown acid.   RECORD. ✳✳✳
   a. use analytical balance — weigh by difference!
   b. does not have to be EXACTLY 0.30g.
3. To each acid sample, add about 30.0 mL H_2O (DI) using graduated cylinder.
4. Stir and break up solid with glass stirring rod. Rinse the stirring rod over the solution with squeeze bottle of DI water.
   C. TITRATING UNKNOWN ACID SAMPLES
1. Add 2 drops phenolphthalein to each sample.
2. Fill burette with standardized NaOH to about 0.00mL mark.
3. Read and record initial volume of NaOH on burette. ✳✳✳
4. Titrate sample #1 to phenolphthalein endpoint.
5. Record final volume of NaOH in burette. ✳✳✳
6. Repeat steps #2 - #5 on Sample #2 and Sample #3.

Pertinent Reactions:
   $HCl + NaOH \longrightarrow Na^+ + Cl^- + H_2O$ (OR) $H^+ + OH^- \longrightarrow H_2O$
(species "HA" denotes unknown acid)
   $HA + NaOH \longrightarrow Na^+ + A^- + H_2O$ (OR) $H^+ + OH^- \longrightarrow H_2O$

16

IMPORTANT: Insert cover flap under yellow copy.

Name: Lisa Smith   Date: 05/26/05

Experiment: Determining the Identity of an Unknown Acid

Observations and Data: Standardization Trials

M of HCl (standardized) = 0.1064 M

Amt. delivered via volumetric pipette = 25.00 mL

Trial #	V_{init} (mL)	V_{fin} (mL)	ΔV (mL)	Mol Acid	Mol Base	M of NaOH (mol/L)
1	0.00	25.00	25.00	2.660×10^{-3}	2.660×10^{-3}	0.1064 M
2	0.15	23.92	23.77	2.660×10^{-3}	2.660×10^{-3}	0.1112 M
3	0.62	24.80	24.18	2.660×10^{-3}	2.660×10^{-3}	0.1100 M

Observations and Data: Preparing Unknown Samples

Appearance of unknown: white flaky powder. Readily dissolves upon addition to H_2O.

Sample #	Mass (g) *
1	0.3011
2	0.2945
3	0.3100

* Note: Analytical balance used. Technique employed = weighing by difference.

Observations and Data: Titrating Unknown Samples

Sample #	V_{init} (mL)	V_{fin} (mL)	ΔV (mL)	M NaOH ($\frac{mol}{L}$)	Mol Base (= Mol Acid)
1	0.00	13.32	13.32	0.1092	1.454×10^{-3} mol
2	13.32	26.43	13.11	0.1092	1.432×10^{-3} mol
3	26.43	40.27	13.84	0.1092	1.511×10^{-3} mol

Sample #	Moles	Mass (g)	Molar Mass
1	1.454×10^{-3}	0.3011	207.1 ← 25.0% (mistake)
2	1.432×10^{-3}	0.2945	205.7
3	1.511×10^{-3}	0.3100	205.1

Unknown Acid Identification = Potassium Hydrogen Phthalate
(a.k.a. KHP)

For all calculations, see "analysis" section.

KHP: Theoretical Molar Mass = 204.23 g/mol

17

IMPORTANT: Insert cover flap under yellow copy.

Name: Lisa Smith   Date: 05/26/05

Experiment: Determining the Identity of an Unknown Acid

Analysis: Sample Calculations

$$\Delta V = V_{fin} - V_{init}$$
$$\Delta V = 13.32 mL - 0.00 mL = 13.32 mL$$

$$moles\ HCl = \underline{M}\ HCl \left(\frac{mol}{L}\right) \cdot Vol\ HCl\ (L)$$
$$moles\ HCl = 2.660 \times 10^{-3} = 0.1064\ M \cdot 25.00 mL / 1000 mL/L$$

$$\underline{M}\ NaOH = moles\ NaOH / (mL\ NaOH / 1000\ mL/L)$$
$$\underline{M}\ NaOH = 0.1064\ \underline{M} = 2.660 \times 10^{-3}\ mol / (25.00\ mL / 1000\ mL/L)$$

$$Average\ \underline{M}\ NaOH = \frac{0.1064\ \underline{M} + 0.1112\ \underline{M} + 0.1100\ \underline{M}}{3} = 0.1092\ \underline{M}\ NaOH$$

$$Molar\ Mass\ unknown = grams\ unknown / moles\ unknown$$
$$MM_{unk} = 0.3011\ g / 1.454 \times 10^{-3}\ mol = 207.1\ g/mol$$

$$Average\ MM_{unk} = \frac{207.1\ g/mol + 205.7\ g/mol + 205.1\ g/mol}{3} = 206.0\ g/mol$$

Analysis: End of Lab Questions

There are no end of lab questions for this experiment.

Analysis: Conclusions

The unknown acid in this experiment was successfully identified as Potassium Hydrogen Phthalate (KHP) via manual titration with standardized NaOH. The experimental Molar Mass of this acid was found to be 206.0 g/mol, which differs from the theoretical molar mass of 204.23 g/mol by only a 0.86% error. Of the two acid identifications to choose from, KHP and Benzoic Acid (molar mass = 122.13 g/mol) the identification of the unknown as KHP is relatively sound considering the very small % error. Overall, the lab was a success as the experimental goal was obtained. In addition, the techniques of pipetting, titrating and working with an indicator were also addressed and mastered.

18

IMPORTANT: Insert cover flap under yellow copy.

Laboratory Conduct and Safety

RULES

1. Goggles and safety aprons or lab coats of the proper design **MUST** be worn at all times anywhere in the lab. A student without goggles and an apron must leave. This is a state law. Goggles and aprons may be rented from 304 CA, the third-floor stockroom.

2. It is strongly suggested that you **not** wear contact lenses to lab; they readily absorb vapors from solvents that are detrimental to the eye. Goggles are not vapor tight and do not completely eliminate this absorption. However, it is your decision. If there is any chance you may wear contacts while in the laboratory, you **MUST** wear a "**I WEAR CONTACTS**" sticker on your lab apron. Note: If you or a neighbor who is wearing contacts get any chemicals in the eye, the contacts are to be removed and thrown away **IMMEDIATELY**, followed by thorough eye washing.

3. Clothing worn to lab must cover legs and feet. You may not wear skirts, shorts, capris, tanktops or spaghetti straps, midriff tops, sandals or open-toed shoes. Loose clothing and long hair should be confined.

4. Avoid skin contact with all chemicals.

5. Pipetting should be done using a rubber bulb and **NOT BY THE MOUTH**.

6. Experiments that produce harmful vapors are to be run under the ventilated hoods in the lab.

7. No smoking, drinking or eating is allowed anywhere in the lab. **Never** put anything in your mouth in the laboratory.

8. Properly dispose of all waste material. Your TA will tell you the approved method of waste disposal for each experiment.

9. Glass must be discarded **ONLY** in the designated containers. Your TA and the lab specialists will inform you regarding glass disposal procedures.

10. Waste paper should be discarded only in designated containers. Waste chemicals and glass should **NEVER** be placed in these containers.

11. **Know** the location of **all** safety equipment. Locate the fire extinguishers, showers, and eye washes in the lab. There are telephones in the stockrooms, in offices, and in the Chemistry Annex Main Office, 107 Chem Annex.

12. Report **all** injuries to the lab instructor and the stockroom personnel, regardless of how minor the injury may seem.

13. Do **NOT** sit on bench tops anywhere, lab or otherwise.

14. Do **NOT** keep extra equipment or shared equipment in the lab drawers.

15. Leave balances **clean**. Shut the doors of the balances after use. Do **NOT** sit on balance tables. Consult a TA if **ANY** difficulty is encountered with the balances.

16. **NEVER** take reagent bottles to your desk. Obtain only the necessary amount of reagent from the bottles in clean test tubes, etc.

17. Don't waste chemicals; only take the amount called for in the lab manual.

18. Do not place pipets in reagent bottles; always pour carefully from the bottle.

19. **BEFORE LEAVING**

    a. You are responsible for cleaning up the area around your sinks and lab bench. Sinks must be free of glass, paper, and debris. Leave **NO** standing water. Benches should be clean and free of equipment. Place Bunsen burners, hoses, clamps and stands neatly on the superstructure above the sinks or in cabinets under the sinks.

    b. Turn off **ALL** gas outlets and water taps.

20. Any **EMERGENCY** (fire, medical, etc.) should be handled by the following procedure:

DIAL 9-911

Tell the Dispatcher:

    a. I need an ambulance (or fire truck) at 601 S. Mathews, the Chemistry Annex Building, Building #10, Room _____.

    b. The phone number here is _____. (Number of phone you used to make the call.)

    c. I will wait by the street for the ambulance (or send someone else!).

Ask the Dispatcher:

Do you need any other information?

21. First aid for any spilled reagent should begin with LOTS of water. Prolonged flooding of the affected area is the first step of treatment for spills on your body.

USE WATER FIRST

For **ACID** burns, you may wash with a sodium bicarbonate solution **AFTER** you have washed with water. NEVER APPLY OINTMENTS OR SALVES TO A BURN WITHOUT A PHYSICIAN'S ADVICE!

Use and Completion of Interactive Video Lessons

ALL IVLs WILL BE AVAILABLE IN THE CHEMISTRY LEARNING CENTER 212 CHEM ANNEX

HOURS
Monday–Thursday 8:30 a.m. –10 p.m.

Friday 8:30 a.m.–5 p.m.

Saturday 10 a.m.– 5 p.m.

Sunday 1 p.m. –8 p.m.

Sign-on Procedure for the Interactive Video Labs in the Chemistry Learning Center

1. Double click on ChemNET icon.

2. Choose your course name on the screen.

3. Type your first name, your last name, your NetID, then click NEXT.

4. Type a password of 10 characters or less which you can remember. Then press RETURN. The first time you do this the computer will ask you to type it again to make sure it is stored correctly.

   After a few seconds, the lesson menu will come up on the screen, and you can choose what you want to work on. The menu items are the interactive video lessons to be completed for the entire semester. You should work all parts of each IVL lesson, but you need not do them all in one sitting. The computer will keep track of the ones you have completed.

   You may need a calculator for some of the lessons.

5. If the Learning Center computer informs you that you are not on the roster for Chemistry 103 IVLs, ask the Learning Center Proctor to add you to the roster. They are at the front desk in the Learning Center.

Interactive Video Laboratory Sets

IVL SET I TOPICS
Elements, Compounds and Mixtures
Chemical Reactions
Chemical Equations
Balancing Equations
Prefixes
Temperature
Mass

IVL SET 2 TOPICS
Pressure
Introduction to PVT
PVT Experiments
Gas Density
Gas Molecular Weight

IVL SET 3 TOPICS
NO_2 Analysis
Orbitals and Electrons
Transition Metal Electrons

IVL SET 4 TOPICS
Introduction to Equilibrium
Chromate-Dichromate
LeChatelier's Principle
Equilibrium Constants
Acids and Bases
Acid-Base Reactions
Metal and Nonmetal Oxides

IVL SET 5 TOPICS
Weak Acids and Bases
Buffers
pH
pH Unknowns
Titration Curves
Titration Experiment

IVL SET 6 TOPICS
Redox Reactions
Redox Practice Problems
Ions in Solution
Net Ionic Equations
Solubility
Solubility Unknowns
Three Beaker Unknowns

EXPERIMENTS IN THE LABORATORY

EXPERIMENTS

Conversion of Aluminum to Aluminum Potassium Sulfate

GOALS

- ■ Practice new lab skills—specifically, proper use of a balance, careful liquid measurement, solution preparation, and filtering and isolation using a Büchner funnel.

- ■ Reinforce topics in class—in this case, conservation of mass and solubility.

- ■ Practice using stoichiometry and calculating percent yield.

Objective

Chemically convert aluminum to aluminum potassium sulfate (alum).

References

Zumdahl, *Chemistry, 6th Edition*, pg. 108–121.

Appendices I. pg 67–72 and II. pg 80,85.

Introduction

Aluminum is hardly a precious metal, on par with gold, silver, or platinum. In fact, it is so common today that we use it for our cheap aluminum foil and soda cans. In the 19th century, however, it was a luxury. Aluminum was made into expensive bracelets alongside gold, and the story is told that Napoleon III favored his most prominent guests by serving them on aluminum dishes, leaving lesser guests to eat off gold. This stark contrast in availability stems from the Hall-Heroult process developed in 1886, allowing the economically viable, commercial production of aluminum. Society was thrilled with this practical new metal, and many household products were made from it—from teakettles to playing cards. Less than a hundred years after the design of this process,

after World War II, the United States found itself with an abundance of aluminum, at which time people even made rugs out of it!

You will have the opportunity to work with this unique metal today. From aluminum foil, you will make a useful compound commonly called alum (specifically, aluminum potassium sulfate, $KAl(SO_4)_2$). There are many practical uses of alum, the product you will be isolating today. It is used industrially in dye manufacture and water treatment. Alum is also used in making paper, cement, and explosives. Interestingly enough, this chemical, with all of its diverse uses, is also employed to pickle cucumbers!

The conversion of aluminum foil to alum involves several chemical steps. In the first chemical step of the experiment, you will add a strong base, potassium hydroxide (KOH), to your aluminum foil. You will heat this mixture on a hot plate. The aluminum and hydroxide will combine to form $Al(OH)_4^-{}_{(aq)}$ and $H_{2(g)}$. The chemical equation for this reaction is shown below:

(handwritten: $\frac{1.39\,mol\,Al}{}\left|\frac{3\,mol\,H_2}{2\,mol\,Al}\right.$)

$$2Al_{(s)} + 2KOH_{(aq)} + 6H_2O_{(l)} \rightarrow 2K^+{}_{(aq)} + 2Al(OH)_4^-{}_{(aq)} + 3H_{2(g)} \qquad \text{Eqn. 1}$$

The next step in the procedure is the addition of sulfuric acid (H_2SO_4), to your sample. Adding acid causes two chemical reactions to occur. First, the $Al(OH)_4^-{}_{(aq)}$ species is converted into $Al(OH)_{3(s)}$, which is a white precipitate. The chemical equation for this conversion is:

$$2Al(OH)_4^-{}_{(aq)} + H_2SO_{4(aq)} \rightarrow 2Al(OH)_{3(s)} + 2H_2O_{(l)} + SO_4^{2-}{}_{(aq)} \qquad \text{Eqn. 2}$$

However, this white precipitate will disappear as the acid is stirred into the solution, as $Al^{3+}{}_{(aq)}$ and water are formed from the reaction of acid with $Al(OH)_{3(s)}$. The second chemical change caused by the addition of acid is:

(handwritten: $\frac{.14g\,Al}{}\left|\frac{1\,mol}{26.98}\right|\frac{2\,mol\,KOH}{2\,mol\,Al} = .0099\,mol\,KOH$)

(handwritten: KOH is in excess)

$$2Al(OH)_{3(s)} + 3H_2SO_{4(aq)} \rightarrow 2Al^{3+}{}_{(aq)} + 3SO_4^{2-}{}_{(aq)} + 6H_2O_{(l)} \qquad \text{Eqn. 3}$$

Finally, we see the formation of hydrated alum crystals ($KAl(SO_4)_2 \cdot 12H_2O_{(s)}$) as the solution is cooled.

(handwritten: $= .00503\,mol\,K^+, Al^{3+}$ need)

(handwritten: $1.26\,g\,Alum\left|\frac{1\,mol\,alum}{474.4g}\right|\frac{1\,mol\,K^+/Al^{3+}}{1\,mol\,alum}$)

(handwritten: 0.1979, .1358)

$$K^+{}_{(aq)} + Al^{3+}{}_{(aq)} + 2SO_4^{2-}{}_{(aq)} + 12H_2O_{(l)} \rightarrow KAl(SO_4)_2 \cdot 12H_2O_{(s)} \qquad \text{Eqn. 4}$$

Note that the alum formed is $KAl(SO_4)_2 \cdot 12H_2O_{(s)}$. The $\cdot 12H_2O$ means that 12 molecules of water are associated with each molecule of the potassium aluminum sulfate. These molecules are the *water of hydration*, and in many compounds are associated with a color change. You will measure this product after it "air dries" but still has its twelve associated water molecules—the water of hydration.

(handwritten: $2.27\,kg\left|\frac{1000g}{1kg}\right|\frac{1\,mol}{474.412g}\left|\frac{1\,mol}{1\,mol}\right|\frac{26.98g}{1\,mol}\left|\frac{1kg}{1000g}\right.$ $= 0.129$? NO.)

(handwritten: 4.39 mol)

(handwritten: $AgNO_3 + NaCl \rightarrow AgCl + NaNO_3$)

(handwritten: $746.29\,g\,AgNO_3\left|\frac{1\,mol}{169.9g}\right|\frac{143.35\,g}{1\,mol\,AgCl} = 629.6684609 = 629.67$)

(handwritten: $.04\,mol\,Al\left|\frac{1}{1\,mol\,alum}\right.$)

Safety

- Never add water to acid. *Always add acid to water*. Sulfuric acid (H_2SO_4) reacts very exothermically with water. The reaction produces a substantial amount of heat. To help you remember this rule, you can use the mnemonic, "Do what you 'oughtter', add the acid to the water."

- Potassium hydroxide reacts with aluminum to produce hydrogen gas, which is very flammable.

- Potassium hydroxide and sulfuric acid are dangerous. They are very caustic, so they will burn you if they come in contact with your skin. If this happens, rinse the exposed area thoroughly with water, and have someone get a TA.

- Ethanol is very flammable. Keep it away from the hot plates and burners!

- Always be aware of your surroundings and others in the lab. Ask a TA if you have any questions.

Procedure

A. SAMPLE PREPARATION

1. Obtain about 0.1 gram of aluminum foil. Your TA will show you an example of a piece that weighs about 0.1 gram.

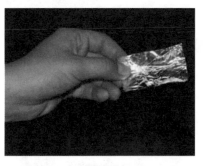

2. Weigh your piece of aluminum foil on an analytical balance. Record the mass in grams in your laboratory notebook to the greatest precision allowed by the balance.

474.4 g
mm of
hydrated alum
crystals

3. Cut the aluminum foil into smaller pieces with scissors, being careful not to lose any.

1

LABORATORY

5

B. ALUMINUM DISSOLUTION AND ALUM FORMATION

1. Place the pieces of aluminum foil in a 50 mL beaker.

2. Measure out 5 mL of 1.4 M KOH in a graduated cylinder. Then pour the KOH into the beaker containing the small pieces of foil. Proper reading of a graduated cylinder is shown in Figure 1-1.

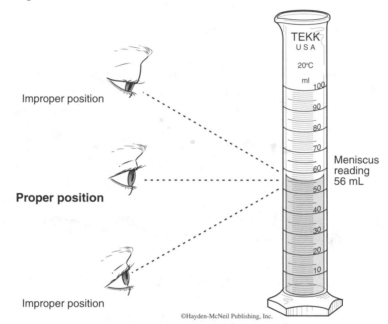

Figure 1-1. Proper Reading of a Graduated Cylinder.

3. Place the beaker with the KOH and small pieces of foil on a hot plate underneath the individual fume hood at your lab bench. It should take about 5 minutes for the aluminum to dissolve with the hot plate set at medium heat. Do not allow the beaker's contents to boil. The solution should turn a dark charcoal gray color.

4. If the liquid level drops to ¼ the initial volume while heating, add some distilled water carefully to bring the level of the liquid back up to ½ of the original volume. Stir occasionally with a glass stirring rod.

5. After 5 minutes on the hot plate, the glass beaker will be hot. Do not attempt to remove it with your bare hands or you will get burned. Use a pair of beaker tongs or an oven mitt to remove the beaker from the hot plate once the aluminum has dissolved. Note the color of the solution at this step.

©Hayden-McNeil Publishing, Inc.

Beaker Tongs

6. Set the beaker aside to cool on your laboratory bench.

7. Measure out 6 mL of 6 M sulfuric acid (H_2SO_4) into a clean graduated cylinder.

8. When your beaker is cool to the touch (this may take several minutes), *slowly* add the 6 mL of the sulfuric acid while *stirring* with a glass stirring rod. This should be done underneath the hood. A pulpy white substance will form; with stirring, however, it should dissolve. This white solid is the precipitate of $Al(OH)_{3(s)}$ discussed in the introduction. Continue to stir until your solution is translucent.

C. CRYSTALLIZATION AND RECOVERY

1. In a medium-sized beaker, make a 50/50 mixture of ice and water. Ice will be provided by your TA.

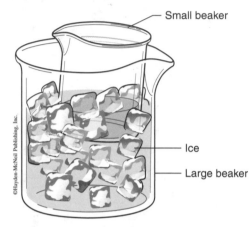

2. Place your beaker into the ice water bath. Cool the solution until the temperature of the liquid in your beaker is about 5°C. Measure the temperature of the solution with the thermometer provided. When it reaches this temperature, add 3 mL of ethanol to your solution using a clean graduated cylinder and cool for 5 more minutes. During this time, you should see white crystals of alum begin forming in your beaker.

3. Set up a Büchner funnel as shown in Figure 1-2. The black ring underneath the Büchner funnel is called a Filter-Vac. It allows a seal to be made between the funnel and the filter flask, and is a necessary part of this set-up. Don't forget to place it beneath your funnel. Secure the filter flask with an iron ring and ring stand, as well.

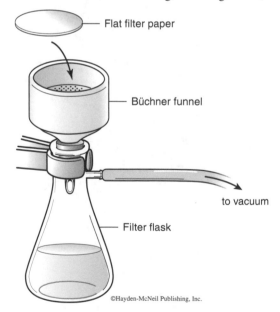

Figure 1-2. Vacuum filtration apparatus.

LABORATORY

1

4. After you have completely set up your apparatus, place a piece of filter paper inside the Büchner funnel. Use your deionized water bottle to wet the paper.

5. Turn on the vacuum. Begin pouring the contents of your beaker through the funnel. Swirl the liquid in the beaker gently to suspend the alum crystals in solution. Continue swirling the beaker's contents and pouring into the funnel until you have filtered all of the solution through the Büchner funnel.

©Hayden-McNeil Publishing, Inc.

6. Make a 10 mL solution containing a 50/50 mixture of ethanol and distilled water in a 50 mL beaker. Again, use a clean graduated cylinder to measure both liquids. Cool this mixture in your ice bath.

7. After it has cooled for a few minutes, use small portions (about 5 mL) of this ethanol/water mixture to rinse the inside of the reaction beaker. Some crystals are probably stuck to the sides and bottom of the beaker. Rinsing the beaker will help you to remove them. Simply add a little ethanol/water rinse solution to the beaker, swirl, and pour this solution into the funnel. The ethanol/water mixture also serves to wash the isolated crystals as they dry.

8. After you are done rinsing, keep the crystals in the Büchner funnel with the vacuum on. Allow air to flow through the filter for 10 minutes. This will help to dry your crystals and remove excess water.

9. Weigh a clean, dry watch glass or weighing boat on the analytical balance. Record the mass in grams in your laboratory notebook to the greatest precision allowed by the balance.

10. Disconnect the hose from the filter flask. Turn off the vacuum.

11. Using a clean, dry spatula, remove the alum crystals from the Büchner funnel and transfer them to the watch glass described above. Weigh the crystals and watch glass. Record the mass in grams in your laboratory notebook to the greatest precision allowed by the balance.

12. Subtract the mass found in step (9) from the mass found in step (11) to find the mass of alum crystals produced. Record the mass of the crystals in your laboratory notebook.

You're done! You have successfully converted common aluminum foil to the useful compound alum. Be sure to clean up your area and dispose of any waste according to your TA's instructions. Answer the following before leaving lab. Ask your TA for help if needed, and feel free to work with your lab partner.

1. How much alum would you have formed if your technique and environment had been ideal, assuming that aluminum is the limiting reactant in this experiment? (Hint: Convert the mass of starting aluminum to moles of aluminum. Then, convert this number into moles of alum. From here, you should be able to calculate the theoretical yield of alum in grams.)

2. What percent of this theoretical yield did you actually isolate according to your measurements? (Hint: Find the percent yield by comparing the answer to #1 and your actual yield of alum crystals in grams.)

Finding the Molar Mass of Butane

GOALS

- Practice your lab skills—specifically, careful liquid measurement and gas collection under water.

- Reinforce topics in class—in this case, gas laws and partial pressure.

- Practice gas law calculations, molar mass determination, and finding percent error.

Objective

Use a lighter to determine the molar mass of butane, and compare this to the accepted value.

References

Zumdahl, *Chemistry, 6th Edition*, pg. 198–207.

Appendices I. pg 69–72 and II. pg 80.

Introduction

"Mr. Zippo," also known as George G. Blaisdell, invented the Zippo™ lighter in 1932. Like many others, he was looking for financial stability during the Depression. Originally, he patterned it after an Austrian lighter, improving the appearance, but these didn't sell. He tried again, this time making it smaller, adding a hinged lid, using what's called a "wind hook" around the wick, and marketing the Zippo™ with the first lifetime guarantee. It sold for $1.95. Since then, these lighters have become extremely popular. Perhaps it is because of their resilience and utility. (One story is told of a Zippo™ that lit on the first try—after being removed from a fish!) Zippos™ are especially known for their utility in war. Soldiers have carried them since World War II, using them for everything from signaling helicopters to storing salt that would replenish what was lost sweating.

Zippo™ lighters are different from everyday, plastic lighters because they contain lighter fluid, not butane. Plastic lighters like the ones you will be using in this lab contain only butane, C_4H_{10}. Why use butane to study gasses and gas laws? First of all, butane is easily collected, as we will show today. Most important, though, is that butane is close to "ideal" at standard temperature and pressure. Ideal gasses are described by the ideal gas law, which states that the product of the pressure and volume of a gas is proportional to the product of the number of moles and the Kelvin temperature. Emil Clapeyron first wrote this in 1834, and we'll write it again here:

$$PV = nRT \qquad\qquad \text{Eqn. 1}$$

R is the gas constant. Its value depends on the units used for the other variables. When pressure is reported in atmospheres (atm), volume in liters (L), and temperature in Kelvin (K), the gas constant has a value of:

$$R = 0.0821 \text{ L·atm/(mol·K)}$$

You will use the ideal gas law to find the molar mass of butane. *Even So* Although butane can be described by the ideal gas law, it is important to remember that it is not ideal. Later on you will use corrections to the ideal gas law to see how butane's behavior deviates from ideal gas behavior.

To find the molar mass of butane, you will collect butane gas by releasing it from a lighter and collecting it over water in a graduated cylinder. You will be able to find the volume of gas released in this way. In addition, you will make measurements of both temperature and pressure. With the volume, temperature, and pressure of butane, you can use the ideal gas law to find the number of moles of butane released from the lighter.

While measuring volume and temperature is accomplished easily, measuring the pressure of the butane gas in the graduated cylinder is more complicated. The relevant gas law that will help you to do this is Dalton's Law of Partial Pressures. It states that a gas exerts a certain pressure regardless of the presence of other gasses. This means that calculating the pressure of each gas in a mixture independently and summing these individual pressures determines the total pressure.

$$P_{total} = P_{gas\ A} + P_{gas\ B} + P_{gas\ C} \qquad\qquad \text{Eqn. 2}$$

Or in our case, since we are collecting the gas over water,

$$P_{atmos.} = P_{butane} + P_{water} \qquad\qquad \text{Eqn. 3}$$

Water vapor pressure (P_{water}) will depend on temperature. Since water is a factor in so many experiments, charts that provide pressure values at common temperatures are readily available (though charts for other gasses can be obtained as well). Such a chart is provided in Table 2-1.

Table 2-1. Vapor Pressure of Water at Various Temperatures

TEMPERATURE (°C)	PRESSURE (ATM)	TEMPERATURE (°C)	PRESSURE (ATM)
17	.0191	24	.0295
18	.0204	25	.0312
19	.0217	26	.0332
20	.0230	27	.0351
21	.0245	28	.0372
22	.0261	29	.0395
23	.0276		

SAFETY

■ Butane is an extremely flammable, colorless gas. Keep this gas away from any type of flame! It is also irritating to the eyes, and harmful when inhaled, so avoid unnecessary exposure. Do this experiment under the hood!

■ Always be aware of your surroundings and others in the lab, and ask a TA if you have any questions.

Procedure

A. LIGHTER PREPARATION

1. Fill a plastic basin about 2/3 full with tap water.

2. Obtain a lighter. Notice that the striking mechanism has been removed for convenience and safety. Wipe the lighter clean and dry with a paper towel. Set the flame adjustment to the largest flame.

3. Weigh the lighter on a balance, and record the mass in grams in your laboratory notebook to the greatest precision allowed by the balance.

©Hayden-McNeil Publishing, Inc.

B. GASEOUS BUTANE COLLECTION

1. Connect the piece of Tygon tubing provided to the lighter. The tubing should fit over the small "spout" where butane is normally delivered to the striking mechanism. The tubing should hug the spout very snugly, so that no gas escapes. If there is not a tight fit between the lighter and the tubing, ask for a new piece of tubing.

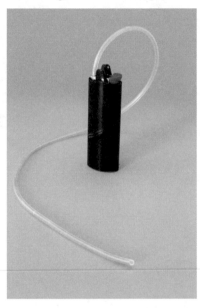

2. Fill a 100 mL graduated cylinder with water. Submerge the graduated cylinder in the plastic basin, and turn it upside down slowly. If any bubbles are present in the cylinder, repeat this step.

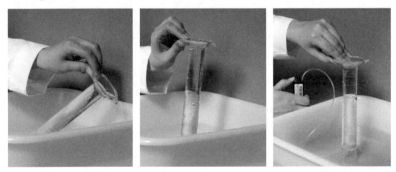

3. While one partner is holding the graduated cylinder upright, the other should feed the end of the tubing that is not attached to the lighter under water and into the graduated cylinder. The tube should extend at least four inches into the cylinder.

LABORATORY

15

4. Press the lever on the lighter while holding the tubing to the lighter with the other hand. After about 10–15 seconds, butane will begin traveling through the tube and into the graduated cylinder. Make sure that all of the gas released is bubbling into the cylinder. If bubbles escape, the experiment must be restarted. You'll know this is happening if you see bubbles coming up through the water in the basin.

5. Continue to hold down the lever until about 75 mL of gas are collected. Then release lever and remove the tubing from the cylinder. Be sure to leave the cylinder upside down in the basin.

C. MEASUREMENT

1. The graduated cylinder has graduations on it that will enable you to read the exact volume of gas that was collected. Before recording the volume of gas collected, make sure that the level of water in the graduated cylinder and the level of water in the basin are even with each other.

2. Carefully read the graduated cylinder, and record the volume of gas collected in your laboratory notebook.

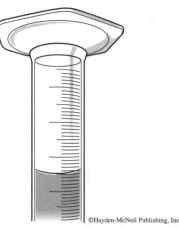
©Hayden-McNeil Publishing, Inc.

3. Thoroughly wipe the lighter clean and dry using a paper towel, and weigh it on the balance. Again, record the mass in grams in your laboratory notebook to the greatest precision allowed by the balance.

4. Measure and record the temperature of the water bath using the thermometer in your laboratory drawer.

5. Record the barometric pressure. The value of the barometric pressure will be provided by the TA.

D. REPEAT THE EXPERIMENT TWO MORE TIMES AND RECORD YOUR SECOND AND THIRD TRIAL RESULTS IN YOUR LABORATORY NOTEBOOK. YOU SHOULD BE ABLE TO USE THE SAME LIGHTER.

2 LABORATORY

Be sure to clean up your area and check with your TA to make sure you have disposed of your lighter properly. You now have all the data necessary to determine the molar mass of butane. Good job! Answer the following before leaving lab. Ask your TA for help if needed, and feel free to work with your lab partner.

1. Using the ideal gas law and your measurements, determine your experimental molar mass of butane. Do this for each trial and average the results. Be sure to show the values you are using (with units), any equations, your results for each trial, and your final result in your laboratory notebook.

2. Calculate your percent error. (Appendix I, page 72) Use the averaged result from above.

$$\% \text{ error} = \frac{|\text{true} - \text{experimental}|}{\text{true}} \times 100$$

Visible Light Spectroscopy

GOALS

- Reinforce topics in class—specifically, the relationships between energy, wavelength, and frequency of electromagnetic radiation.

- Investigate the visible spectrum of helium and hydrogen using a spectroscope.

- Investigate the visible spectra of the following ions by flame test: Na^+, Ca^{2+}, Ba^{2+}, Sr^{2+}, and K^+.

Objectives

- Identify the spectral lines of hydrogen that fall in the visible region of the electromagnetic spectrum.

- Analyze an unknown salt containing one of the ions listed above.

- Use the Rydberg equation in calculating ΔE for electronic transitions occurring in an atom containing only one electron.

References

Zumdahl, *Chemistry, 6th Edition*, pg. 290–299 and A18–A21. See also *Figures 7.7 and 7.8 in Sections 7.3 and 7.4.*

Appendices I. pg 72–75 and II. pg 79–80.

Introduction

Spectroscopy is the study of the interaction of electromagnetic radiation and matter. What is electromagnetic radiation? It is any form of radiant energy that is propagated as waves, and includes what we commonly call "visible light." Electromagnetic radiation is character- ized by the wave properties of frequency (ν), wavelength (λ), and velocity (c). All electro- magnetic radiation travels in a vacuum at a constant velocity: $c = 3.00 \times 10^8$ m/s, the speed of light.

For light waves, the frequency and wavelength are inversely related, and their product is equal to velocity:

$$\nu\lambda = c$$

Eqn. 1

Frequency is generally measured in Hertz—cycles per second (written 1/sec or sec^{-1}). Wave- length can be measured in any unit for length, but nanometers (1 nm = 1×10^{-9}m) and meters are most common.

The energy (E) of electromagnetic radiation is directly proportional to its frequency:

$$E = h\nu$$

Eqn. 2

where h is Planck's Constant, equal to 6.626×10^{-34} J•sec/photon. Energy (E) is measured in Joules/photon. Thus, given any one of the three parameters, frequency, wavelength, or energy, the other two can be calculated.

You might have noticed that Equation 1 talked about electromagnetic radiation as a wave, and that Equation 2 referred to individual particles—photons. Scientists have determined that it is best to think of electromagnetic radiation as being both wave-like and particle-like (they call this wave/particle duality). This is why you will sometimes hear Equation 1 ap- plied to a photon and Equation two applied to a wave. Both are correct!

The entire range of wavelengths of electromagnetic radiation is known as the electromag- netic spectrum, shown in **Figure 3-1**.

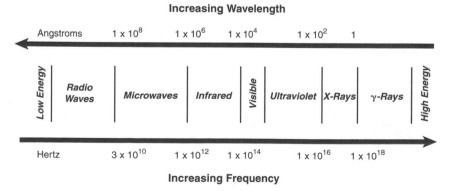

Figure 3-1: The Electromagnetic Spectrum

3 LABORATORY

As we can see from **Figure 3-1**, the electromagnetic spectrum is made up of many different kinds of radiation, from low frequency, low energy radio waves with long wavelengths to high frequency, high energy gamma rays with short wavelengths. In actuality, there is no strict division between wave types. Categories and divisions are simply convenient approximations. It is important to remember that the electromagnetic spectrum is a continuum. This experiment targets the visible region of this spectrum specifically, because we can see electromagnetic radiation with wavelengths in this region with our own eyes!

Spectra are observed when matter emits photons. You will observe this phenomenon during your experiment. When an object emits light, it is acting as a source of radiation. Examples of light-emitting objects include a red-hot iron bar and the glowing tungsten filament of an electric light bulb. In order for an object to emit radiation, however, it must first absorb energy from another source. In this experiment, the energy sources you will use to cause emission are electric current from a power supply and heat from a burner flame.

Matter also absorbs electromagnetic radiation. We are witness to this phenomenon everyday. Each kind of matter absorbs certain characteristic frequencies of radiation; the frequencies absorbed cannot be detected by the eye. Therefore, the color of an object is indicative of what wavelengths of visible light are not being absorbed by the object. For example, a red apple is absorbing all wavelengths of visible light except those in the red region. Therefore, the apple appears red.

One of the earliest clues that changed much of how we think about elemental substances was borne of spectroscopy, the study of emitted and absorbed light by matter. In 1885, Angstrom excited atomic hydrogen and recorded a series of visible lines that were emitted. The spectrum found was much different from the "rainbow" spectrum one sees when looking at white light through a prism. Instead, the spectrum of atomic hydrogen contains a few narrow bands or lines of specific colors. Like hydrogen, each element has its own unique emission spectrum that consists of only a few narrow lines. This emission spectrum serves as a "fingerprint" for each element. Therefore, examining emission spectra is among the very best ways to identify the elements in samples as varied as seawater and distant stars.

It might seem that spectroscopy is only a qualitative way of identifying different materials, but it is quite handy for quantitative measurements, too. Modern atomic orbital theory began with the excitation of an element's atoms by Angstrom, and has matured today to include the following important principles about atoms:

1. Electrons of an atom have only certain allowed energies, and each of these energies is associated with a particular atomic orbital. It is by this description that we can also say that the energy of electrons is quantized.

2. The electrons in atoms are contained in particular orbitals.

3. All orbitals, and thus the electrons in them, are associated with a particular energy, E.

4. Only certain orbitals, and thus only certain energies, are allowed. Each of these allowed orbitals is assigned an integer, n, known as the principal quantum number.

5. When light is absorbed, an electron "jumps" from one allowed energy level (orbital) to another. The energy corresponding to this "jump" is described as ΔE, or the difference in energy from the lower state to the higher state. The absorbed light has a wavelength corresponding to ΔE.

6. **For hydrogen**, this electronic transition energy can be mathematically described by the Rydberg equation:

$$\Delta E = R_H(1/n_{2initial} - 1/n_{2final}) \qquad \frac{1}{n_f{}^2} - \frac{1}{n_i{}^2} \qquad \text{Eqn.3}$$

Where $R_H = 2.18 \times 10^{-18}$ J/photon, and $n_{initial}$ and n_{final} are the principal quantum numbers of the initial and the final energy levels, respectively.

If photon emission occurs, $n_{initial} > n_{final}$, and ΔE will be negative. If a photon is absorbed, $n_{initial} < n_{final}$, and ΔE will be positive.

Let's look at an example for clarification. An electron could be in hydrogen's lowest state ($n = 1$, the ground state). Then, it absorbs a very specific amount of energy and is elevated to a higher energy orbital (say, $n = 3$). The Rydberg equation would describe ΔE as positive, because $n_{initial} = 1$ and $n_{final} = 3$. Then, the atom emits this energy, as the electron "falls" from $n = 3$ to $n = 1$. The Rydberg equation gives a negative ΔE for this transition, as now $n_{initial} = 3$ and $n_{final} = 1$.

This model explains why the frequencies of light absorbed are exactly equal to the frequencies of light emitted by a hydrogen sample. Electrons simply move from one energy level to another, either "up" or "down". Note that this also explains why emission only occurs after absorption of energy from another source; electrons must be excited above $n = 1$ for emission to occur.

Use of the Rydberg equation is permissible for all atoms or ions with one electron. The general equation includes a term, Z, for atomic number. For hydrogen, $Z = 1$. For all atoms or ions, Z is a positive integer. The general Rydberg equation is:

$$\Delta E = R_H Z^2(1/n^2_{initial} - 1/n^2_{final}) \qquad \text{Eqn. 4}$$

Today, you will use the Rydberg equation when determining the spectral lines of the hydrogen emission spectrum. You will also look at the spectral lines and emission spectra of other elements as well.

The instrument you will use to study spectra is variously called a spectroscope, spectrograph, or a spectrometer. Broadly, two types of spectrometers exist. An emission spectrometer is used to analyze light emitted from an excited source. An absorption spectrometer is used to analyze light reflected by or transmitted through matter.

3

LABORATORY

A diagram of the spectroscope you will use today is shown in **Figure 3-2**. The slit regulates the amount of light that enters the spectroscope and thus the width of the resulting spectral lines. Light entering the slit passes through the spectroscope to the diffraction grating located in the eyepiece. Light passing through this grating is separated into its components. The scale, which is visible through the eyepiece, is illuminated by the light entering the spectroscope from a second direction. Thus, you will see the spectrum superimposed upon the scale, which is marked off in units of angstroms ($1\text{Å} = 1 \times 10^{-10}\text{m}$).

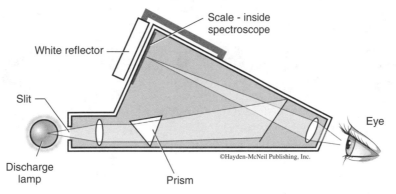

Figure 3-2: Diagram of a Spectroscope

Safety

When using spectrometers and gas discharge tubes, the following safety issues apply:

- The gas discharge tubes become extremely hot when used with the power supplies. You should be careful not to touch them until they have cooled.

When doing the flame tests, the following safety issues apply:

- Working with an open flame presents fire hazards; keep long hair and loose clothing tied back.

- The metal spatulas used to introduce chemicals into the flame can become very hot. Be careful when handling these.

- Each container of reagent has its own spatula. Do not use a spatula from one reagent to test a different reagent. For instance, the spatula used to dispense sodium chloride should not be used to dispense any other chemical. This will eliminate contamination and make unknown identification easier for everyone.

Procedure

Today, the class should split into two groups. Half of the class will begin part I of the experiment while the other half begins with part II. Once you and your partner have finished with one part, you may move on to the next, provided there is equipment available.

PART I: QUANTITATIVE EXAMINATION OF THE EMISSION SPECTRA FOR HYDROGEN AND HELIUM

A. SPECTROSCOPE CALIBRATION

1. The calibration of your spectroscope is necessary to correct for systematic error. This is done by comparing **your** experimentally-determined wavelengths to wavelengths obtained from the literature. A convenient source of emission lines is the helium discharge tube.

2. Proceed to the station with the helium tube in the power supply. A helium tube in a power supply is shown in figure 3-3. Note the color of the discharge tube in your notebook. Look through the eyepiece of your spectroscope and find the six helium lines. Note the position of these lines with regard to the scale and record their colors and their wavelengths in Angstroms in your laboratory notebook.

Figure 3-3. A helium tube in a power supply.

A diagram of the emission spectrum for helium is shown in Figure 3–4.

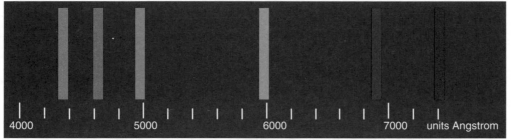

Figure 3-4. Diagram of the emission spectrum of helium.

3. Readings are dependent upon the position of your eye. Therefore, one person should take the readings and should be consistent with the position of their eye relative to the eyepiece. Both you and your partner must look through the spectroscope, however.

4. Prepare a calibration plot by graphing the scale reading obtained experimentally on the x axis versus the literature wavelength values for helium emission on the y axis. The theoretical values of these lines are:

data table ?

COLOR OF LINE	THEORETICAL WAVELENGTH IN ANGSTROMS
Blue-Violet	4471
Blue	4713
Green	5015
Orange	5875
Red-Orange	7065
Dark Red	7281

5. You must use a full sheet of paper in your laboratory notebook for the plot. This plot will be used to calculate the corrected wavelengths for the hydrogen spectrum and will be different for each spectroscope. Therefore, take data carefully, and be sure to use your own scope.

B. THE HYDROGEN ATOMIC SPECTRUM

1. Proceed to a station with a hydrogen discharge tube in the power supply. Or, if you are going to use the same power supply for this step, ask your TA to switch the He tube for a H_2 tube. Note the color of the discharge tube in your notebook. Look at the hydrogen discharge tube with your spectroscope just as you did for the helium discharge tube. Again, although both group members must view the spectrum, only one should take data in order to be consistent. Make sure that your eye position is consistent relative to the eyepiece.

3

LABORATORY

Figure 3-5. A hydrogen tube in a power supply.

4104 4800   6050 6640

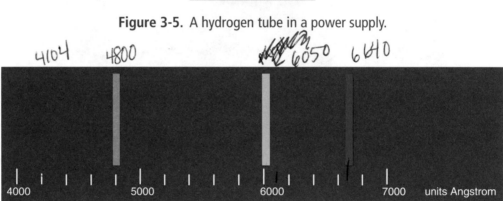

Figure 3-6. Diagram of the emission spectrum of hydrogen.

2. Describe what you see in the spectroscope. Include the number of lines, the color, and the wavelength of each line in Angstroms. The fourth line for the hydrogen spectrum may or may not be visible; its actual wavelength is 4104 Angstroms. Record the color and experimental wavelength for the fourth line if it is visible. Calculate the frequency and energy of each line (see End of Lab Questions) using the corrected wavelengths.

PART II: QUALITATIVE EXAMINATION OF EMISSION SPECTRA FOR VARIOUS METAL IONS

A. FLAME TESTS ON KNOWN METAL IONS

1. Now that you have quantitatively measured the emission spectra for various atoms, you will have the chance to qualitatively observe the emissions of several excited metal ions.

2. To view the emission spectra of metal ions, energy must be applied to excite the electrons into higher energy levels. Just as electricity was applied to the discharge tubes, heat must be applied to a small amount of each metal chloride salt. You will put a spatula containing a metal salt into a burner flame and observe the emission with your eyes.

3. Proceed to the flame test stations. At each station, there should be a crystalline metal chloride salt, a burner, and a spatula. Place a small amount of the solid in the spatula, and heat it in the flame of the burner. Observe and record the color of the flame in your lab notebook.

4. Move on to the other flame test stations and repeat the above procedure until you have viewed all of the salts. Observe and note the emission color for Na^+, K^+, Ca^{2+}, Sr^{2+} and Ba^{2+}.

5. Clean the lab bench free of scattered salts.

B. FLAME TEST FOR UNKNOWN IDENTIFICATION

1. Obtain an unknown from your TA. Record the number of your unknown. Obtain a spatula and clean it thoroughly with soap and water. Rinse with tap water. Then, rinse well with deionized water and dry.

2. Heat your unknown in a burner flame as you did for the known metal chloride salts. Record the color of your unknown and compare it to those from the known solids to determine which ion is present in your unknown sample.

3. Carefully rinse the spatula with deionized water after it has cooled until any remaining solid is dissolved, and return it to the community property.

4. Clean the work area of scattered salts.

safety

27

3
LABORATORY

When you have completed both sections, you're finished with the laboratory portion of this experiment. Well done! You have observed several atomic spectra and experimentally determined the identity of an unknown cation. Answer the following before leaving the laboratory. Ask your TA for help if needed, and feel free to work with your lab partner.

1. Using the calibration plot that you made with the helium emission tube, correct the experimentally determined wavelengths for the four visible lines of the hydrogen spectrum. Report these corrected values.

2. Calculate the frequency and energy (in joules) for each hydrogen spectral line you observed using the wavelengths found and the equations given in the introduction.

3. Reproduce and fill in the following table in your lab notebook, where $n_{initial}$ and n_{final} are principal quantum numbers. For each set of $n_{initial}$ and n_{final} values, calculate $n^2_{initial}$, n^2_{final}, $(1/n^2_i - 1/n^2_f)$, and $\Delta E = R_H(1/n^2_i - 1/n^2_f)$ (for hydrogen, $Z = 1$).

$N_{INITIAL}$	N_{FINAL}	$N^2_{INITIAL}$	N^2_{FINAL}	$(1/N^2_i - 1/N^2_f)$	ΔE
3	1				
4	1				
3	2				
4	2				
5	2				
6	2				

4. What energy transitions did you observe for hydrogen electrons by using the spectroscope? In other words, from what energy level to what energy level did the electron transition? Use your answers to questions 2. and 3. to help answer this question.

5. Calculate percent error using the theoretical energy values calculated in the above chart and experimentally determined energy values from your experiment. (Appendix I, page 72)

6. Report the identity of your unknown to your TA. write in conclusion

K+

6.17

3

LABORATORY

28

Investigation of Systems at Equilibrium

GOALS

■ Continue to hone laboratory skills—specifically, microscale techniques you will employ today.

■ Reinforce topics in class—particularly the concept of equilibrium as a "dynamic" process.

■ Explore and predict how equilibrium systems will respond to different stresses according to Le Châtelier's principle.

Objective

Use Le Châtelier's principle to explain your observations of several equilibrium systems as they respond to temperature and concentration changes.

References

Zumdahl, *Chemistry, 6th Edition*, pg. 242–264 and 609–642.

Appendices II. A. and II. B. in this manual.

Introduction

What is equilibrium? The word "equilibrium" describes the reaction conditions where, at the same time reactants are forming products in the "forward" direction, the products are undergoing a chemical change to form reactants in the "reverse" direction. At equilibrium, the rate of the forward reaction is equal to the rate of the reverse reaction, and thus the interchange of reactants and products is constant. The system is in a state of balance, and even though both the forward and the reverse reactions are occurring simultaneously, the concentrations of all substances in the system remain constant.

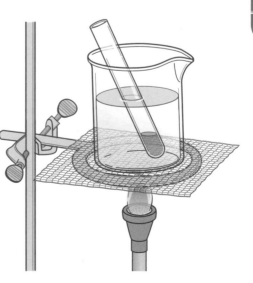

The process of equilibrium governs many of the chemical reactions taking place in the human body. Specific enzymes work this way. An enzyme is a very, very large molecule in the body that works as a catalyst—it lowers the energy barrier of a reaction so that it can proceed at a faster rate. Without the enzyme, some reactions of the human body might take up to one million years to spontaneously occur! Sometimes, the near impossible job of speeding up reactions operates under the process of equilibrium. In many biochemical processes, the enzymes in our body catalyze both the forward and reverse reactions they are designed to "speed up." Therefore, our cells do not over-produce certain chemicals and always have reactants to convert into products in the forward direction when needed.

The behavior of any system at equilibrium, including those catalyzed by certain enzymes in the body, follows Le Châtelier's principle. Le Châtelier's principle predicts that if a "stress" is applied to a system at equilibrium, the system will adjust toward a new equilibrium state in a direction that reduces the stress.

Today you will examine three equilibrium systems. You will apply different stresses to each system, including changing the concentration of one of the substances involved or the temperature. You will predict, using Le Châtelier's principle, which way the equilibrium will shift to accommodate the stress. Then, after observing the change in the system, you will note whether or not this change follows Le Châtelier's principle.

Safety

- All of the solutions used today are potentially hazardous. Some are irritating to the skin and can cause severe burns if spills or splashes are not properly treated. Notify your TA immediately if your skin comes into contact with any of the chemicals used today. Rinse affected areas under cool water for fifteen minutes.

- As always, use gloves, goggles, and aprons to protect yourself.

- The chemicals used today should not be poured down the sink. Your TA will point out the waste carboys where you should dispose of waste.

Procedure

PART I: EQUILIBRIUM SYSTEMS STRESSED BY CHANGING ION CONCENTRATIONS

A. IRON(III) THIOCYANATE FORMATION

1. First, you will examine the equilibrium resulting from the combination of Fe^{3+}, ions and thiocyanate, SCN^-, ions. The equilibrium expression for the formation of iron(III) thiocyanate is as follows:

$$Fe^{3+}_{(aq)} + SCN^-_{(aq)} \rightleftarrows FeSCN^{2+}_{(aq)} \qquad \text{Eqn. 1}$$
$$\text{(Reddish Brown)}$$

2. Using a clean graduated cylinder, add 25 mL of 0.0020 M $KSCN_{(aq)}$ to a 100 mL beaker. To this solution, add 25 mL of deionized water, again using a clean graduated cylinder. Note the color of the solution and record this information in your laboratory notebook. ✳

3. Add 5 drops of 0.02 M $Fe(NO_3)_{3(aq)}$ to this solution using a Pasteur pipet. The Pasteur pipets will be provided in the laboratory. Mix and note the color of the solution. ✳

Pasteur pipet

4. You will stress the resulting equilibrium system in three different ways. Pour approximately 5 mL of this solution into four clean, dry test tubes.

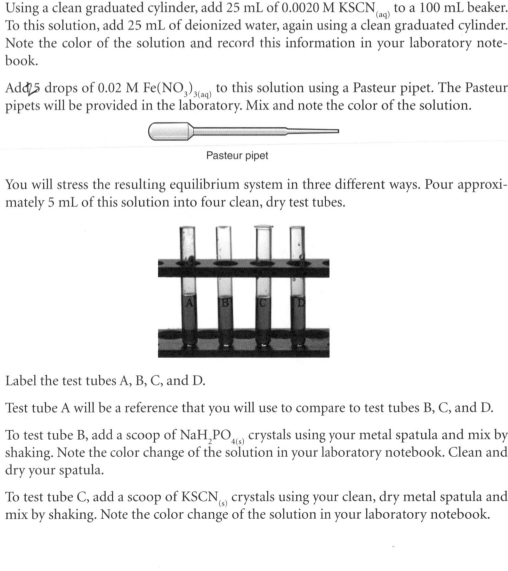

5. Label the test tubes A, B, C, and D.

6. Test tube A will be a reference that you will use to compare to test tubes B, C, and D.

7. To test tube B, add a scoop of $NaH_2PO_{4(s)}$ crystals using your metal spatula and mix by shaking. Note the color change of the solution in your laboratory notebook. Clean and dry your spatula. ✳

8. To test tube C, add a scoop of $KSCN_{(s)}$ crystals using your clean, dry metal spatula and mix by shaking. Note the color change of the solution in your laboratory notebook. ✳

• O2

9. To test tube D, add 10 drops of 0.20 M $Fe(NO_3)_{3(aq)}$ using a Pasteur pipet and mix by shaking. Note the color change of the solution in your laboratory notebook.

10. In your laboratory notebook, designate which additions of ions above caused a shift in equilibrium. Describe whether or not the observed shift in equilibrium followed the prediction of Le Châtelier's principle. BE SPECIFIC! Your TA will be looking for the color change noted, the reason for the color change, and specifically whether or not this change indicates that the system is following Le Châtelier's principle.

11. Dispose of the contents of each test tube in the appropriate waste carboy. Clean and dry the test tubes before moving on to the next section.

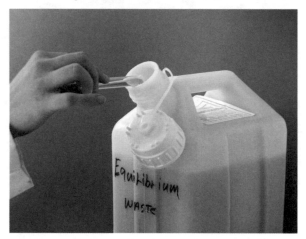

B. THE HEXAAQUOCOBALT(II) – TETRACHLOROCOBALT(II) SYSTEM

1. You will be examining the hexaaquocobalt(II) – tetrachlorocobalt(II) equilibrium described by the following expression:

$$4Cl^-_{(aq)} + Co(H_2O)_6{}^{2+}_{(aq)} \rightleftharpoons CoCl_4{}^{2-}_{(aq)} + 6H_2O_{(l)} \qquad \text{Eqn. 2}$$

(Pink)   (Blue)

2. Using a clean, dry graduated cylinder, pour 3 mL of ethanol into a clean, dry test tube, and label it test tube A.

3. Clean the graduated cylinder with deionized water.

4. Pour 3 mL of deionized water using the graduated cylinder into a second test tube, also cleaned and dried. Label this test tube B.

5. Before adding a small scoop of cobalt(II) chloride, $CoCl_{2(s)}$ into test tubes A and B, describe the solid in your notebook. Then predict what color each of the resulting solutions will be. Write down your predictions in your laboratory notebook.

6. Add the solid cobalt(II) chloride to each test tube using a clean, dry metal spatula. Stopper each tube and shake to dissolve the solid in solution. Make sure the solid is completely dissolved before proceeding. Observe and note the colors of each solution. Were your predictions correct? Record whether or not your predictions were correct and whether or not the observed changes were predicted by Le Châtelier. Be specific!

©Hayden-McNeil Publishing, Inc.

7. Using a Pasteur pipet, slowly and carefully add 3 mL of water to test tube B. The pipet tip should nearly rest on the bottom of the test tube. Do you note a color change? Does the color of the resulting solution indicate that Le Châtelier's principle was obeyed?

8. Now, carefully and slowly add 3 mL of water into test tube A, making sure that the pipet tip nearly rests on the bottom of the test tube. Record your observations in your laboratory notebook. What phenomena do you observe? Does this change follow Le Châtelier's principle or not? You may need to discuss with your TA, instructor, or other groups regarding this step.

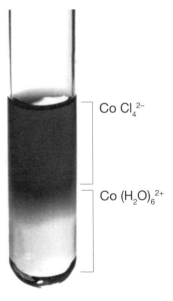

$Co\,Cl_4^{2-}$

$Co\,(H_2O)_6^{2+}$

4

LABORATORY

33

9. Do not disturb the contents of test tube A by shaking or jarring. Try to maintain the separation being observed. In your notebook, include a short comparison of the densities of ethanol and water.

10. Dispose of the contents of test tube B in the appropriate waste carboy. Keep test tube A for the next section.

PART II: EQUILIBRIUM SYSTEM STRESSED BY CHANGING TEMPERATURES

C. THE HEXAAQUOCOBALT(II) – TETRACHLOROCOBALT(II) SYSTEM REVISITED

1. You will again be examining the hexaaquocobalt(II) – tetrachlorocobalt(II) equilibrium described by the following expression:

$$4Cl^-_{(aq)} + Co(H_2O)_6^{2+}_{(aq)} \rightleftarrows CoCl_4^{2-}_{(aq)} + 6H_2O_{(l)} \qquad \text{Eqn. 2}$$
$$\text{(Pink)} \qquad\qquad \text{(Blue)}$$

2. Create an ice water bath by filling a large beaker with tap water and ice (the ice will be provided by your TA).

3. Place test tube A into this ice bath.

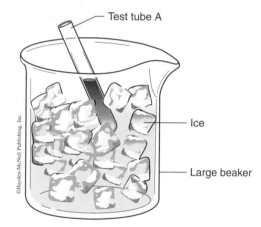

Test tube A

Ice

Large beaker

©Hayden-McNeil Publishing, Inc.

4. Allow 5–10 minutes to pass while the test tube cools in the ice bath. During this time, use Le Châtelier's principle to predict what color changes will occur. Also, predict if the ✗ reaction is endothermic or exothermic (see your text, section 6.1, for help). Note the color change observed after this time in your laboratory notebook.

5. Place test tube A in a 250 mL beaker that is half-filled with tap water. Place the beaker atop a wire gauze square and iron ring over a Bunsen burner as shown in **Figure 4-1** or a hot plate set to medium heat.

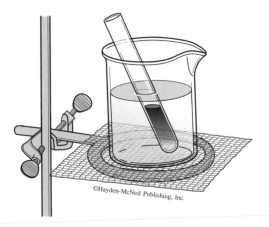

©Hayden-McNeil Publishing, Inc.

Figure 4-1. Heating Test Tube.

6. Heat the water bath until the water is hot but not boiling. After 5–10 minutes, note the ✗ change in solution color.

7. In your laboratory notebook, note how the equilibrium shifted with the addition of heat.

8. Turn off the Bunsen burner and allow the water bath to cool.

9. Dispose of the contents of test tube A in the appropriate waste carboy. Clean and dry the test tube and all of the other unwashed glassware before leaving the laboratory.

✳ Safety ✳

Once you have cleaned up your station and replaced all of your equipment in the proper place, you're finished! You've learned how Le Châtelier's principle can be used to predict how an equilibrium system will change with the addition or removal of chemicals or heat.

Determination of CO_2 Composition in Pop Rocks™ Candies

GOALS

■ Develop laboratory skills and techniques—primarily using a pipet and a buret.

■ Understand the purpose of titrations—specifically, why they are used in calculating the amounts of different substances.

■ Reinforce topics in class—in this case, acid-base chemistry and writing balanced chemical equations.

Objectives

▪ Complete two manual titrations.

▪ Find the amount of carbon dioxide contained in 1 gram of the infamous candy, "Pop Rocks™".

References

Zumdahl, *Chemistry, 6th Edition*, pg. 158–164 and 744–749.

Appendices II. pg. 80–84.

Introduction

There are many myths surrounding the ever-popular Pop Rocks™ candy. The fizzy, gas-producing candy seems to be the stuff of urban legend and tall tale! When Pop Rocks™ candy first became commercially available in the mid-nineteen seventies, the stories of torn-open tummies and Coca-Cola™ induced explosions had parents literally panicked. Several Poison Control centers actually had to create emergency phone lines to assist hysterical parents and assure them that their children would not be harmed by the fizzing candy.

How did such a myth begin? Because Pop Rocks™ fizz and pop when they are put into the mouth, parents believed that their children might be ingesting the gas created and that their stomachs could be seriously harmed—they even thought their children might explode! And although this myth is totally unfounded (eating Pop Rocks™ might not be nutritious, but it certainly won't cause you to detonate), there is some truth to the way these parents were thinking about Pop Rocks™.

Pop Rocks™ are formed by the addition of sugar and other sweet ingredients to a pressurized chamber filled with carbon dioxide, CO_2. The carbon dioxide/candy mixture is heated to excesses of 320 degrees Fahrenheit and then super-cooled under extremely high pressures (50 atm or more!). Upon relieving this huge pressure, the mass of candy fractures into tiny "rocks". The "rocks" contain pockets of the CO_2 gas originally introduced into the mixture. Therefore, when Pop Rocks™ dissolve in your mouth, the gas is released from the pockets with a popping sound.

Your job in lab today will be to determine the amount of carbon dioxide per gram of the candy. You will do this by dissolving the Pop Rocks™ slowly and collecting the CO_2 gas that escapes. However, the lab is unequipped to measure small amounts of gas accurately, so you will convert the CO_2 gas into a measurable quantity. By using 0.1 M $NaOH_{(aq)}$, you will convert the gas to sodium carbonate, $Na_2CO_{3(aq)}$. If this chemical could be isolated, one could then calculate the moles produced via a balanced chemical equation like the one below:

$$2Na^+_{(aq)} + 2OH^-_{(aq)} + CO_{2(g)} \rightleftarrows 2Na^+_{(aq)} + CO_3^{2-}_{(aq)} + H_2O_{(l)} \qquad \text{Eqn. 1}$$

However, since you are collecting an unknown amount of $CO_{2(g)}$, it is not clear how much NaOH should be used to covert $CO_{2(g)}$ into $CO_3^{2-}_{(aq)}$. Therefore, after the above reaction takes place, you will have some NaOH left over. The major species in the collection vessel will be Na^+, CO_3^{2-}, and OH^-.

You will titrate this mixture twice with $HCl_{(aq)}$. In the first titration, you will use the indicator phenolphthalein, which is pink in basic solution and clear in acidic solution. In the second titration, you will use methyl orange. Methyl orange is a red liquid which will be yellow-orange at the beginning of the second titration and will turn red at the endpoint of the titration.

Two reactions will take place with the addition of acid in the first titration. The excess OH^- will be neutralized, and the carbonate ion, $CO_3^{2-}_{(aq)}$, will be converted to bicarbonate, $HCO_3^-_{(aq)}$. These two reactions are shown below:

$$OH^-_{(aq)} + H^+_{(aq)} \rightleftarrows H_2O_{(l)} \qquad \text{Eqn. 2}$$

$$CO_3^{2-}_{(aq)} + H^+_{(aq)} \rightleftarrows HCO_3^-_{(aq)} \qquad \text{Eqn. 3}$$

After the first titration, the major species in solution is the bicarbonate ion, $HCO_3^-{}_{(aq)}$. You will titrate this ion using $HCl_{(aq)}$ to form the species $H_2CO_{3(aq)}$ in the second titration.

The reaction is as follows:

$$HCO_3^-{}_{(aq)} + H^+{}_{(aq)} \rightleftarrows H_2CO_{3(aq)} \qquad\qquad \text{Eqn. 4}$$

The amount of $H_2CO_{3(aq)}$ formed is exactly equal to the amount of $CO_{2(g)}$ evolved from your sample of Pop Rocks™. Why?

To answer this question, you should consider all of the reactions involved. In the second titration (Equation 4), the $HCl_{(aq)}$ reacts only with the $HCO_3^-{}_{(aq)}$. Since they react in a one-to-one ratio and you measure how much HCl you add, you can easily determine the amount of $HCO_3^-{}_{(aq)}$ formed. Then, Equation 3 shows that $HCO_3^-{}_{(aq)}$ is related to $CO_3^{2-}{}_{(aq)}$ in a one-to-one ratio as well. Taking another step backwards, Equation 1 shows us that $CO_3^{2-}{}_{(aq)}$ is related to $CO_{2(g)}$ by *another* one-to-one ratio. Calculating the original amount of carbon dioxide is made significantly easier since the coefficients in all the balanced equations are one. If they were not, it would certainly be possible to relate the moles of starting and ending materials to each other, but the stoichiometry would be more complicated.

When you have found the amount of $CO_{2(g)}$ evolved by the Pop Rocks™, you have completed the main objective for this lab!

Safety

■ The indicators used in this lab, methyl orange and phenolphthalein, are harmful if swallowed. In addition, they can be irritating to the skin. If any indicator is splashed on your skin, rinse with cool water for five minutes.

■ NaOH and HCl are very dangerous chemicals that can cause severe burns. If your skin comes in contact with either NaOH or HCl solution, rinse with cool water for 15 minutes and alert your TA.

■ Any spills of reagents should be reported to the TA immediately.

■ Although it may be tempting to eat your Pop Rocks™ sample, remember that it is considered contaminated because it was introduced into the laboratory environment. Do not eat your sample.

Procedure

A. COMPLETING A PRACTICE TITRATION/DETERMINATION OF M OF HCL

1. Add 10 mL of standardized NaOH to a 100 mL Erlenmeyer flask using a clean graduated cylinder.

2. Add 2 drops of phenolphthalein to the flask. Swirl. The solution should be bright pink.

3. Clean a 50 mL buret with tap water and then deionized water.

4. Close the stopcock on the bottom of the buret.

5. Set up the buret in a ring stand and buret clamp as shown in Figure 5–1.

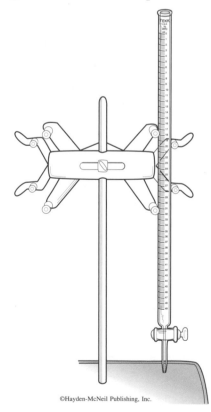

©Hayden-McNeil Publishing, Inc.

Figure 5-1. Buret in buret clamp on ring stand.

5 LABORATORY

6. Rinse the buret with about 10 mL of 0.1 M HCl. This is often called "priming" the buret. The purpose is to completely wet the inside of the buret with the titrant.

7. Fill the buret with 0.1 M HCl slowly, using a graduated cylinder and a funnel.

8. Place a "Waste" beaker beneath the buret.

9. Slowly open the stopcock and allow about 5 mL of HCl to drip slowly into the "Waste" beaker. During this time, you should manipulate the stopcock so that you get comfortable adding HCl in drops. See Figure 5-2.

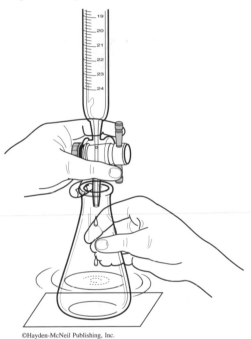

©Hayden-McNeil Publishing, Inc.

Figure 5-2. Manipulating the stopcock of a buret.

10. RECORD THE INITIAL VOLUME ON THE BURET. IT DOES NOT HAVE TO BE 0.00 mL.

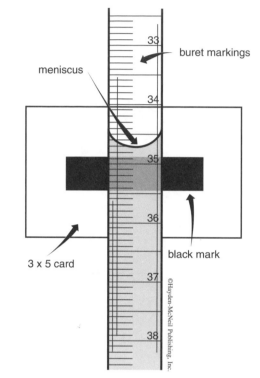

11. Place the flask containing NaOH underneath the buret.

12. Slowly add HCl to the flask, a few drops at a time, with plenty of swirling.

13. Continue adding HCl slowly until a very faint pink color is achieved. This is the end-point of your titration.

14. RECORD THE FINAL VOLUME ON THE BURET. Calculate the molarity of HCl.

15. Add 2 drops of methyl orange to the flask. Swirl. The solution should be yellow-orange.

16. Slowly add HCl to the flask, a few drops at a time, with plenty of swirling.

17. Continue adding HCl slowly until a very deep reddish/pink color is achieved. This is the endpoint of your titration.

18. RECORD THE FINAL VOLUME ON THE BURET.

5
LABORATORY

B. EVOLUTION OF CARBON DIOXIDE FROM POP ROCKS™

1. Obtain two 50 mL Erlenmeyer flasks and a distillation tube (shown in **Figure 5-3**). Your TA will come around to pass out the Pop Rocks™ samples. You should receive one package of Pop Rocks™.

2. Clean and dry one of the 50 mL Erlenmeyer flasks and place it on the balance.

3. Tare the balance.

4. Carefully pour the entire Pop Rocks™ sample into the flask. Record the mass in grams in your laboratory notebook to the greatest precision allowed by the balance.

5. Into the other 50 mL Erlenmeyer flask, introduce 30.0 mL of standardized $NaOH_{(aq)}$ using a graduated cylinder. The NaOH provided has been standardized by the laboratory staff so that the concentration is accurately known. You must record the molarity of NaOH as indicated on the bottle in order to complete the calculations for this experiment.

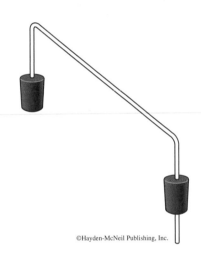

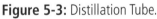

©Hayden-McNeil Publishing, Inc.

Figure 5-3: Distillation Tube.

6. Set up the distillation-type apparatus shown in **Figure 5-4**. The flask containing Pop Rocks™ should sit atop a wire gauze pad above a Bunsen burner or hot plate. Be sure that the boiling flask sits level on the gauze pad or hot plate. The flask containing the NaOH, the receiving flask, should rest inside of a 250 mL beaker. The two will be connected by the distillation tube.

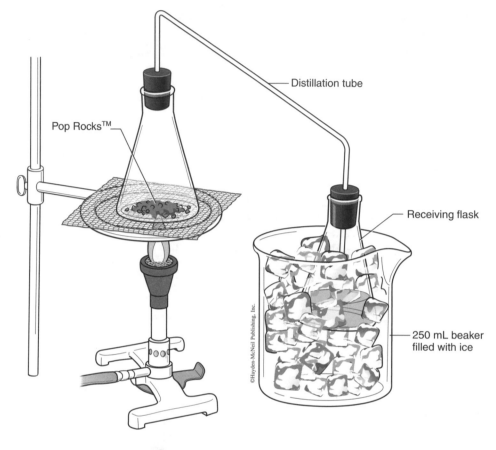

Distillation tube

Pop Rocks™

Receiving flask

250 mL beaker
filled with ice

©Hayden-McNeil Publishing, Inc.

Figure 5-4: Distillation Setup.

The 250 mL beaker should be filled with ice until the receiving flask is completely covered. The distillation tube should be immersed in the NaOH solution, so that when gas bubbles into the receiving flask, it will be introduced into the solution, not the air above the solution. If you wish, you may ask your TA to check your setup before you begin.

7. Pour about 25 mL of deionized water on top of your Pop Rocks™ sample and VERY quickly replace the distillation head.

8. Turn on the burner and heat the Pop Rocks™/water solution.

9. Allow the Pop Rocks™ to dissolve in the solution until the reaction flask stops fizzing and bubbling. All of the solid Pop Rocks™ sample should be completely dissolved. No solid candy should be visible in the boiling flask.

10. While the reaction is taking place, refill your 50 mL buret with ~0.1 M $HCl_{(aq)}$. By completing the practice titration you have found the molarity of HCl. Use this molarity for the rest of your experimental calculations.

C. FIRST TITRATION

1. Once the fizzing has stopped, take the receiving flask off of the apparatus immediately. Then turn off the hot plate. Swirl the receiving flask a few times. Use your deionized water bottle to squirt water through the distillation tube and into the receiving flask. Then pour the contents of the receiving vessel (the one originally containing NaOH) into a clean, dry 250 mL beaker. Rinse the receiving flask with a small portion of deionized water. Add the rinse water into the beaker. Add 2–3 drops of phenolphthalein.

2. Record the initial volume on the buret to the nearest hundredth of a milliliter. It does not have to be exactly 0.00 mL.

3. Titrate the solution from the receiving vessel to the endpoint with HCl. Add the HCl solution from the buret a few drops at a time. Swirl the beaker in between additions. You have reached the endpoint when the solution is a very light shade of pale pink. It may help to place a white sheet of paper under your flask. To be sure that you have reached the endpoint, you should compare your beaker with one the TA will provide, showing the correct color of the phenolphthalein endpoint.

4. Record the final volume on the buret to the nearest hundredth of a milliliter.

D. SECOND TITRATION

1. Add 2–3 drops of methyl orange to the beaker.

2. Refill the buret to about the 25.00 mL mark with HCl if needed. Record the initial volume to the nearest hundredth of a milliliter. Again, the initial volume does not have to be exactly 25.00 mL.

3. This titration will take considerably less HCl to complete.

4. Titrate the solution to the endpoint again; the methyl orange should turn red. Again, add the HCl solution from the buret slowly, a few drops at a time. Swirl the beaker in between additions. A sheet of white paper may be useful here, as well, to help determine the endpoint. To be sure that you have reached the endpoint, you should compare your beaker with one the TA will provide, showing the correct color of the methyl orange endpoint.

5. Record the final volume on the buret to the nearest hundredth of a milliliter.

      — Pertinent Equations
      — Safety

You've completed a distillation and two manual titrations. You now have the tools to successfully determine how much carbon dioxide is contained in one gram of Pop Rocks™. Answer the following before leaving the lab. Ask your TA for help if needed, and feel free to work with your lab partner.

1. Calculate the molarity of your HCl from the results of the practice titration.

2. Calculate the moles of HCl added during the first titration and during the second titration. Since you have recorded the volumes added during each titration and you already know the molarity of the HCl you used, these should be straightforward calculations.

3. What is the number of moles of $HCO_3^-{}_{(aq)}$ produced in this experiment? The number of moles of $CO_3^{2-}{}_{(aq)}$ produced? The number of moles of $CO_{2(g)}$ produced?

4. What is the number of liters of $CO_{2(g)}$ produced by your sample of Pop Rocks™ candy? Hint: There are 22.4 L of carbon dioxide/mol.

5. What is your experimental value of milliliters of carbon dioxide per gram of Pop Rocks™ candy?

5

LABORATORY

47

Determining the identity of Unknown Compounds

GOALS

- Develop your laboratory skills—specifically, small-scale technique and observation.

- Reinforce topics in class—especially four main reaction types (redox, precipitation, acid-base, and complexation).

- Practice writing both complete and net ionic equations.

Objectives

- Determine the behavior of Universal Indicator.

- Identify solutions as acidic, basic, or neutral.

- Describe the products of several reactions. *using solubility rules,*

- Deduce the identity of unknown compounds. *knowledge of acids/bases*

References

Zumdahl, *Chemistry, 6ᵗʰ Edition*, pg. 133–155, 160–178.

Introduction

Deducing the identity of unknown compounds has been a central aspect of chemistry for hundreds of years. However, before early chemists could have any references for identification, they had to come up with systems of classification. Moving away from taxonomies that described everything as different ratios of Earth, Water, Air, and Fire, they divided species up as gasses, solids, and liquids; they declared sour compounds acids and bitter compounds bases; the categories go on and on. With increasingly sophisticated taxonomies, and a grow-

Purpose
Principles based on
Techniques / chem principles

ing understanding of atoms, elements, and molecules, chemists were able to place new un-identified compounds in appropriate categories. We still do this today. Think of forensics. Chemists are needed to identify drugs, determine what chemicals remain on bomb frag-ments, and find the cause of a fire among arson debris.

Today, you will deduce the identity of three unknowns based on your observations and what you know of chemical properties and reactivity. Like a forensic scientist, you'll do diagnostic "tests" on known samples and compare these "tests" to an unknown sample's behavior. The procedure that you are about to undertake has helped scientists, including forensic chemists, identify the unknown contents of water samples, soil samples, and even specimens of human remains!

You will be performing a lot of different reactions in this lab period, but don't let the sheer number overwhelm you. While each combination of reagents will behave in a unique way, we can categorize them all fairly easily.

Let's investigate the following categorization of chemical reactions:

Precipitation reactions occur when two or more compounds in a solution react to form a new, insoluble compound (the precipitate) that "falls out" of solution. This is perhaps the easiest type of reaction to identify visually. For example, when clear solutions of potassium iodide and lead(II) nitrate are combined, a bright yellow solid appears as if from nowhere. What happened? To understand this, we'll need to turn to *chemical equations and solubility rules.*

Given our reagents, we have the following:

$$KI_{(aq)} + Pb(NO_3)_{2(aq)} \qquad\qquad \text{Eqn. 1}$$

To form our reactants, we do a double exchange, essentially a "repairing." A simple ex-ample makes this clear. Notice that all the compounds (both reactants and products) are made of a **cationic** and an **anionic** component.

$$\mathbf{AB} + \mathbf{CD} \rightleftarrows \mathbf{AD} + \mathbf{CB} \qquad\qquad \text{Eqn. 2}$$

In terms of our original reaction, we form:

$$2\mathbf{KI}_{(aq)} + \mathbf{Pb(NO_3)}_{2(aq)} \rightleftarrows 2KNO_3 + PbI_2 \qquad\qquad \text{Eqn. 3}$$

We're almost there. All we have to do now is determine which product is insoluble, and thus the yellow precipitate. In order to do so, we will turn to the solubility rules you have learned about in lecture and read about in your chemistry text.

Table 6-1. Solubility Rules

SOLUBLE	INSOLUBLE	EXCEPTIONS
Most nitrates (NO_3^-) and ammonium (NH_4^+) compounds		
Most Group I compounds		
Most chloride, bromide, and iodide (Cl^-, Br^-, I^-) compounds		Compounds that also contain silver, lead, or mercury (Ag^+, Pb^{2+}, Hg_2^{2+}) are insoluble
Most sulfates (SO_4^{2-})		Compounds that also contain barium, lead, mercury, or calcium (Ba^{2+}, Pb^{2+}, Hg_2^{2+}, Ca^{2+}) are insoluble
	Most hydroxides (OH^-)	Compounds that also contain Group I elements and ammonium are soluble, and compounds that also contain Group II elements are marginally soluble
	Most sulfides, carbonates, chromates, and phosphates (S^{2-}, CO_3^{2-}, CrO_4^{2-}, PO_4^{3-})	Compounds that also contain Group I elements or ammonium (NH_4^+) are soluble

This table is adapted from Zumdahl, *Chemistry, 6th edition*, Table 4.1, pg. 152.

So we see that while KNO_3 is soluble, PbI_2 is not, and must be the yellow solid.

$$2KI_{(aq)} + Pb(NO_3)_{2(aq)} \rightleftarrows 2KNO_{3(aq)} + PbI_{2(s)} \qquad \text{Eqn. 4}$$

A step further will allow us to simplify this equation dramatically. The aqueous (aq) subscript indicates that a species is soluble in water, and exists mainly as ions. Therefore, we write:

$$2K^+_{(aq)} + 2I^-_{(aq)} + Pb^{2+}_{(aq)} + 2NO_3^-_{(aq)} \rightleftarrows 2K^+_{(aq)} + 2NO_3^-_{(aq)} + PbI_{2(s)} \qquad \text{Eqn. 5}$$

6

LABORATORY

Then, we cancel out the species that appear on both sides of the equation. Essentially, these do not change or participate during the reaction. They are called *spectator* ions. Without the spectator ions written, we have the *net ionic equation*:

$$2I^-_{(aq)} + Pb^{2+}_{(aq)} \rightleftarrows PbI_{2(s)}$$

Eqn. 6

You will observe many reactions of this type today, and you can use this procedure on each one.

Acid-Base Reactions. For our purposes, there are two ways of thinking about acids and bases. In the *Arrhenius* definition, acids produce protons (H^+) in water, and bases produce hydroxide ions (OH^-). It is a straightforward and useful definition for many cases, but it doesn't include all acids and bases. The *Brønsted-Lowry* concept describes acid-base reactions as the transfer of a proton from one compound to another. A molecule that **donates** a proton is called an acid, and a molecule that accepts a proton is called a base.

$$H - \overset{..}{\underset{..}{Br}}: + \overset{H \quad H}{\underset{}{:O:}} \longrightarrow \overset{H}{\underset{H \quad H}{|O|}} + :\overset{..}{\underset{..}{Br}}:^-$$

Eqn. 7

We see that HBr is the acid because it gives up a proton, and that H_2O is the base because it accepts the proton. In equation form, we write:

$$HBr_{(aq)} + H_2O_{(l)} \rightleftarrows Br^-_{(aq)} + H_3O^+_{(aq)}$$

Eqn. 8

Often, you will see this reaction written in a simpler form. The idea is the same, however.

$$HBr_{(aq)} \rightleftarrows H^+_{(aq)} + Br^-_{(aq)}$$

Eqn. 9

This equation reflects the fact that HBr can be described with the Arrhenius definition of an acid, as well as the Brønsted-Lowry definition.

HBr is a fairly simple case. You will come across reactions that are more difficult to write. The key is to remember that for it to be an acid-base reaction, one compound has to gain a proton, and the other has to lose one. But what if you can't tell by looking which species will donate and which will accept? What if you have a reaction between ammonia (NH_3) and water? Both contain hydrogen atoms that could be donated, and both can accept protons as well. Experimentally, we sometimes use indicators. Indicators are substances that respond differently to acidic and basic solutions—generally in terms of color. For example, phenolphthalein is a common indicator that turns pink in basic solutions and is clear in acidic solutions. In this lab, you will use Universal Indicator. Just like phenolphthalein, its color depends on the acidity of the solution. The trick is that you will have to figure out how!

Complexation Reactions are a little complicated, but that's not the source of their name. A complexation reaction can be described as a reaction that forms a "complex." For instance, in adding a cobalt salt, such as $CoCl_2(s)$, to water, we form $[Co(H_2O)_6]^{2+}_{(aq)}$. The part of this substance written in brackets is called a complex ion; it involves more than one species but still carries an overall charge (making it an ion) while in solution. The entire group has a charge, much like a polyatomic ion. Examples of complex ions include species such as $[Cu(CN)_2]^-$ and $[Mn(H_2O)_6]^{2+}$. The list below helps describe complexation reactions in more detail:

- Complexes generally form around a transition metal cation (ex: Ni^{2+}, Au^{3+}, Cu^+).

- Whether or not a complex forms depends on concentration, among other factors. A reaction between two compounds may proceed normally until it is "flooded" by one of the reagents, at which point a complex ion is more likely to form.

- The formation of a complex is generally indicated by a color change. In fact, most complex ions are very brightly colored.

- Don't worry! You won't be expected to figure out the formulas for any complex ions you create.

Redox Reactions (**oxidation reduction reactions**) involve the transfer of electrons. One species is oxidized, and loses electrons, while another is reduced, and gains electrons.

A useful way to remember this is with the mnemonic: **Leo says Ger**

Loss of **e**lectrons = **o**xidation.

Gain of **e**lectrons = **r**eduction.

Let's look at an example:

$$2Al_{(s)} + 3Zn^{2+}_{(aq)} \rightleftarrows 2Al^{3+}_{(aq)} + 3Zn_{(s)} \qquad \text{Eqn. 10}$$

It may not look unusual at first, but this isn't like the other reactions we've seen. No atoms are moving from one compound to another, and nothing is dissociating. We need a way to explain how **solid aluminum and zinc ions** transformed into **aluminum ions and solid zinc**. To do this, chemists break the reaction into two half reactions, one for each element.

$$Al(s) \rightleftarrows Al^{3+}_{(aq)} + 3e^- \qquad \text{Eqn. 11}$$

$$Zn^{2+}_{(aq)} + 2e^- \rightleftarrows Zn_{(s)} \qquad \text{Eqn. 12}$$

6

LABORATORY

53

Equation 11 is an oxidation reaction; each mole of solid aluminum loses three moles of electrons to become a mole of aluminum cations. Equation 12 is a reduction reaction; each mole of zinc cations gains two moles of electrons to become a mole of solid zinc. It's important to note that for a reaction to occur there must be *both oxidation and reduction*. One species can only lose electrons if another species is in solution to take them.

It isn't always obvious from observation alone that a redox reaction is taking place, but keep the option in mind. If you observe a reaction, and you can't think of a combination of anions and cations that could form new products, consider redox before you give up.

Safety

■ While you are using only small quantities of reagents, many chemicals in this lab are potentially hazardous. Rinse thoroughly with cool water if any reagents come into contact with your skin. Alert your TA.

■ Be especially cautious around the reagents station. Accidents can be more dangerous where more chemicals are present and there is some crowding.

■ Always put the lids of each reagent bottle or jar on tightly when you are done. Never pick up a container by the lid.

■ Always wear your goggles and apron. You may also wish to wear gloves.

■ Always be aware of your surroundings and others in the lab. Ask a TA if you have any questions.

Procedure

The actual procedure for this experiment is relatively simple, but be sure to read through all the information before the specific instructions in each section.

A. ORGANIZING YOUR EXPERIMENT

There are two charts at the end of this experiment. These are labeled *reactions* and *unknowns*. They'll help you keep track of everything throughout the lab. You will make similar ones yourself.

1. Remove the charts from the end of this experiment.

2. Place the *reactions* chart between stiff paper and a transparency sheet. The stiff paper provides a flat surface, and the transparency is a good reaction surface. Once you have this set up, you may want to tape down the edges to keep it all in place. Set the other chart aside for now.

3. Get out two well trays. One will be for the reagents and the other for your microburets. Place a sheet of paper underneath each well tray.

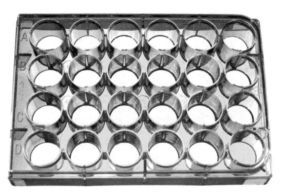

Well Tray

4. Label one sheet so that you can keep track of what reagent you put in each well. How you do this is up to you—just make sure it's straightforward enough that you won't be confused later. Then fill each well with some reagent, according to your chart. Your TA will tell you where to get these compounds.

5. Label the paper under the other tray the same way. To avoid contamination during the experiment, you'll have one microburet for each reagent, and you can keep them all in the second well tray. Store the microburet in the well labeled with the reagent it will contain. This should avoid contamination and allow you to find what you need quickly. Label the individual microburets as well.

LABORATORY

55

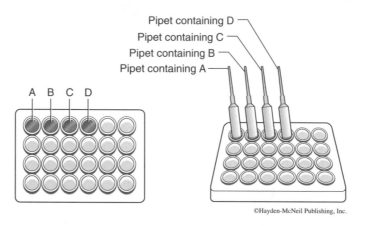

Pipet containing D
Pipet containing C
Pipet containing B
Pipet containing A

A B C D

©Hayden-McNeil Publishing, Inc.

6. The importance of good and thorough observations during this lab cannot be stressed enough. You will need to use the results from each section to properly complete other parts of the experiment, so it's in your own best interest to be neat and organized. The following tips will help keep your experiment running smoothly.

- Organize your observations in tables.

- Create a system of abbreviations for colors, precipitates, gas formation, etc. Be sure to make a key so others can follow your work (and so you can remember later!) Your key should look like this:

OBSERVATIONS KEY	
Ppt	Precipitate
CR	Clear
CLD	Cloudy
(g)	Gas
dp, dps	Drop, drops
etc.	…

- The following is an example of how you might organize parts B and C of this experiment. You will need several tables like the chart below to record all of your observations. Notice that this chart looks just like your *reaction* chart, but leaves more space for your observations. Every cell should be filled. (The observations are not what you will see; we don't want to spoil anything for you!)

- **Don't forget to include the concentration of each reagent in your tables!**

- Don't make your tables too small. There's no reason to try to fit everything on one page.

- Remember, tables like these should be made *before* you come to lab, so you can spend your time on the reactions themselves.

PARTS B AND C: DETERMINE THE BEHAVIOR OF UI/DESCRIBE THE PRODUCTS OF REACTIONS				
	0.1 M $FeCl_3$	0.1 M $CuSO_4$	0.1 M KI	0.1 M H_2SO_4
Compound alone				CLR
UI		GR-YE color change		
0.1 M H_2SO_4	no visible change/ xn. Suspect A-B rxn, 2 dps $FeCl_3$ + 1 dp UI = dark BL–GN			
0.1 M KI	no visible change/ rxn. Adding 2 more dps KI—golden YE ppt.			

7. Here are some tips for running reactions:

- Be sure to combine reagents in the appropriately labeled area of the chart. This will avoid confusion.

- Each cell of the chart is half black and half white. Try to center the reaction on the dividing line. Having both a dark and a light background behind your reaction will make it easier to see the variety of gasses, precipitates, and colors that form.

- To run a reaction, add a couple drops of the first reagent, then a drop or two of the second. Be sure not to touch the tip of the microburet to other solutions or the plastic. You may need to add another drop of one solution or the other, and you can stir with a small stirring rod (be sure to rinse this with distilled water and wipe dry between uses).

- To clean up an individual reaction, use an extra microburet to suck up the reaction and then discard it into a waste beaker. Then use a cotton swab to clean and dry the area.

- If you want to clean off the entire sheet, add some water and pour the entire mixture into your waste beaker. Rinse well with deionized water and dry with a paper towel.

6

LABORATORY

57

B. DETERMINE THE BEHAVIOR OF THE UNIVERSAL INDICATOR (UI)

Later in the experiment, you'll run several acid-base reactions. The only way to track their progress is using an indicator. As discussed in the introduction, indicators change color depending on the acidity or basicity of the solution. What you have to do now is determine how Universal Indicator behaves. You'll determine this by tracking its behavior in known acids and bases. Then you will use this information to test all your reagents to see which are acidic, basic, and neutral.

1. Place a drop of each of your known acids on your reaction chart. Add a drop of UI to each one and record your observations in your laboratory notebook.

2. Do the same with any compounds you know are bases.

3. Potassium iodide (KI) will be neutral. Add universal indicator to a drop of this as well to see how it behaves in neutral solution.

4. Now that you know the behavior of UI, use it to test the remaining solutions and record your observations. Keep track of whether each solution is acidic, basic, or neutral.

5. Record your conclusions about the behavior of UI and the acidity/basicity of each compound in your laboratory notebook immediately after mixing.

C. DESCRIBE THE PRODUCTS OF SEVERAL REACTIONS

Here you will look at the results of each combination of two reagents. Take careful observations! Note color changes, formation of precipitates, and formation of gasses (indicated by bubbles). Rushing through this part will make your unknown determination harder. Of course, feel free to experiment. Add another drop of one or both reagents if you can't see anything at first, and don't forget to stir.

> **HELPFUL HINTS**
>
> Often times, reactions in which nothing appears to happen are acid-base reactions. When you run into this, clean the reaction cell. Place a couple drops of the first compound back on the cell, add a drop of UI, and record the color. Then, add a drop of the other reagent. If you are observing an acid-base reaction, the pH will change, and so UI will change color as well.
>
> When you react copper sulfate ($CuSO_4$) with ammonia (NH_3), add one drop of the copper sulfate to a few drops of ammonia. Observe. Then add a few more drops and observe again. There should be a change.
>
> Run all the reactions with ammonia before you complete any other reactions. Ammonia is volatile (it has a high vapor pressure and evaporates quickly) so it can affect other nearby reactions. Once you have done the ammonia reactions, you can clean off your transparency sheet and proceed with the rest of your investigation.

1. Before you run any reactions, record your observations about the compounds themselves.

2. Mix the reagents in pairs according to the reaction chart.

3. Record your observations in your laboratory notebook.

6 LABORATORY

#3

D. DEDUCE THE IDENTITY OF UNKNOWN COMPOUNDS

In this portion of the lab you will have three unknowns to identify. One will be one of the compounds you have already worked with, one will contain an anion you've worked with, and another a cation you've worked with in this lab. *Be sure to record the number of each unknown in your laboratory notebook.*

The latter two may be more difficult to determine because the observations may not match perfectly with the set of observations for any one compound. For the cation unknown, the anion may be different from your known solutions. For the anion unknown, the cation may be different from your known solutions.

You'll have to think carefully about what happens during reactions, but you have several ways to determine your unknowns. Really, your experimental procedure is up to you!

It is very important that you *write down what you do* to determine the identity of your unknowns. Be specific! Record what compounds you react, why, what you observe, and what you can conclude. Be organized and thorough. Someone else should be able to recreate your experiment from your notebook (without reference to this manual).

1. Set up another reaction chart. This time use the *unknowns* chart. It has a lot of room for you to experiment.

2. You will also want to label the wells in which you keep your unknown microburets, as well as the microburets themselves.

3. Observe the color of your unknowns.

4. Test each unknown with Universal Indicator.

5. Mix each unknown with your known compounds.

6. Binary mix your unknowns with each other.

7. You may want to redo some of the known reactions for comparison.

8. When you think you know the identity of your compounds, show your results to your TA.

9. Write the reactions by which you have identified your unknowns. Net ionic equations are appropriate.

✳ pertinent reactions
✳ safety concerns

END OF LAB QUESTIONS

There is no Post-Lab quiz (MC or FR) for this lab. These questions, completed in lab and turned in with your lab report, take the place of a Post-Lab quiz.

color "alone"

1. Describe the behavior of Universal Indicator, and state whether each compound is acidic, basic, or neutral.

2. Write the reaction between ammonia (NH_3) and hydrochloric acid (HCl). Be sure to include all subscripts and balance the equation. (Hint: Use the Brønsted-Lowry definition of acids and bases.)

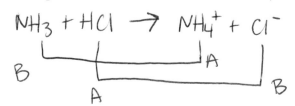

cation - Fe^{3+}
anion - CO$_3^{2-}$
unknown

3. Choose your two favorite precipitation reactions from this lab. For each, follow the procedure outlined in the introduction to write a complete and a net ionic equation for each. Be sure to include all subscripts and balance the equations.

4. You are in chemistry lab, and you've forgotten to label two of your beakers. You know one is aqueous silver(I) nitrate ($AgNO_3$), and the other is aqueous ammonium nitrate (NH_4NO_3). What could you add to a small sample of each beaker's contents to determine the identity of your solutions? Explain.

5. Which reaction during the lab was a complexation reaction? What makes you think this?

6. What gas made up the bubbles you saw in a few of your reactions? Think about the combination of reactants that tended to produce this gas. What seem to be the requirements to form it?

7. Using the procedure you used for precipitation reactions, try to write a net ionic equation for the reaction between potassium iodide (KI) and copper(II) sulfate ($CuSO_4$). What goes wrong?

It turns out this is a redox reaction. Look at the balanced reaction below and the two half reactions that make it up. Identify which compound is being reduced and which is being oxidized.

$$2Cu^{2+}_{(aq)} + 2I^-_{(aq)} \rightleftarrows I_{2(s)} + 2Cu^+_{(aq)} \qquad \text{(balanced reaction)}$$

$$Cu^{2+}_{(aq)} + e^- \rightleftarrows Cu^+_{(aq)} \qquad \text{(half reaction)}$$

$$2I^-_{(aq)} \rightleftarrows I_{2(s)} + 2e^- \qquad \text{(half reaction)}$$

REACTIONS

	H$_2$SO$_4$	KI	CuSO$_4$	FeCl$_3$	Ba(NO$_3$)$_2$	Na$_2$CO$_3$	NH$_3$	NaOH	HCl
UI									
H$_2$SO$_4$									
KI									
CuSO$_4$									
FeCl$_3$									
Ba(NO$_3$)$_2$									
Na$_2$CO$_3$									
NH$_3$									
NaOH									

6

LABORATORY

61

UNKNOWNS

	HCl	NaOH	NH$_3$	Na$_2$CO$_3$	Ba(NO$_3$)$_2$	FeCl$_3$	CuSO$_4$	KI	H$_2$SO$_4$	UI
Unknown #1–#9										
Cation Unknown										
Anion Unknown										

Test Area			

6

LABORATORY

63

APPENDICES

APPENDICES

Treatment of Scientific Data

Units and Conversions

All measurements contain two parts: a **number**, which shows the magnitude of an effect; and **units**, which provide a basis for the comparison of a measured quantity with a reference standard.

There are several systems of units in use, two of which, the so-called "British" and "metric" systems are most familiar. In 1969, a comprehensive system was introduced by the scientific community called the "Système International d'Unités," abbreviated "SI." This system is closely related to the metric system but is more clearly defined.

To go from one system to another requires a **conversion factor**. The following is a list of common quantities used in the laboratory along with the units most often used to specify them. Some conversion factors are also listed.

QUANTITY	METRIC UNIT	SI UNIT
mass	gram (g)	kilogram (kg) = (1000 g)
time	second (s)	second (s)
volume	milliliter (mL)	cubic meter (m^3) = (106 mL)
length	centimeter (cm)	meter (m) = (100 cm)
pressure	torr, mm Hg	pascal (Pa) = (9.87×10^{-3} atm)
	(1 atm = 760 torr)	
temperature	°C	K (°C + 273)
heat	calorie (cal)	joule (J) = (0.239 cal)
work	calorie	joule (J)

Units are most often chosen with regard to the magnitude of the quantity measured. For example, it is not convenient to express the mass of a locomotive in grams; kilograms would be a better choice.

THE UNITS OF A QUANTITY MUST ALWAYS BE GIVEN.

I

Dimensional Analysis

A very powerful technique for solving problems involving units is **dimensional analysis**, or analysis of units. For example, if you live 3500 meters from campus and can run this distance in 12 minutes, what is your average speed in miles/hour? The units themselves suggest how the problem may be solved.

Since the example asks for speed, and since the answer is in units of (distance)/ (time), divide the number of meters (distance) by the number of minutes (time) to get m/min:

$$\text{speed} = \frac{3500}{12 \text{ min}} = 292 \text{ m/min}$$

Then use conversion factors to arrive at the proper units, miles/hour:

$$\frac{292 \text{ m}}{\text{min}} \times \frac{60 \text{ m}}{\text{hour}} \times \frac{1 \text{ mile}}{1610 \text{ m}} \times \frac{10.9 \text{ miles}}{\text{hour}} = 11 \text{ miles/hour}$$

Exponents And Scientific Notation

Scientists often work with very large or very small numbers which can be cumbersome to write. The speed of light is 30,000,000,000 cm/sec; the mass of a single carbon atom is 0.00000000000000000000001992g. Calculations involving such quantities may be simplified by expressing them as numbers between 1 and 10, times 10 raised to some power ($\times 10^x$). 100 is 1×10^2, 0.00001 is 1×10^{-5}, 62,380 is 6.238×10^4, and 0.0795 is 7.95×10^{-2}. In scientific notation, the speed of light is expressed as 3.0×10^{10} cm/sec, and the weight of one carbon atom is 1.992×10^{-23} g. The power of ten is the number of places which the decimal point must be moved to yield a number between 1 and 10. To convert the population of Chicago, 3,607,000, to scientific notation, the decimal point is moved 6 times, giving 3.607×10^6. Only significant figures are used in scientific notation, thus removing the ambiguity of the final zero(s).

Calculating with numbers in scientific notation is not difficult, but requires some care. Exponential numbers may be added and subtracted only when the exponents are the same. $(1.05 \times 10^3) + (2.36 \times 10^3)$ gives 3.41×10^3, but to add 1.05×10^3 and 2.36×10^2, one of the exponents must be changed: to either $(1.05 \times 10^3) + (0.236 \times 10^3)$ or $(\mathbf{10.5 \times 10^2}) + (2.36 \times 10^2)$ to give 1.29×10^3.

In multiplying two numbers expressed in exponential notation, multiply the coefficients and then add the exponents: $(5.0 \times 10^3) \times (1.6 \times 10^2) = 8.0 \times 10^5$. To divide, divide the coefficients, then subtract the exponents.

Logarithms

Logarithms are another use of exponential notation which were developed to make calculations easier. You will use logarithms in Chemistry 103. For example, the strength of an acid is defined in terms of "pH," which is the negative logarithm of the hydrogen ion concentration of a solution.

$$pH = -\log[H^+]$$

The logarithm (log) of a number, N, is the exponent to which 10 must be raised to equal the number N. For example, the log of 100 is 2, since $10^2 = 100$. If $10^x = 2.45$, then $x = 0.389$ since $10^{0.389} = 2.45$. The log of a number should be expressed with the same number of figures to the right of the decimal point as the number has significant figures.

To find the number whose log is given, you must calculate the antilog of the number. If the log (x) = 2, then x must equal 100. If the given value of a log contains decimals and is not as straightforward as the example log(x) = 2, you can employ a calculator or a log table.

Significant Figures in Measurements and Calculations

The numbers recorded for a measurement in the laboratory depend on the **precision of the measuring device**. For example, using a typical multiple beam balance, the mass of a beaker might be reported as 60.51, but with an analytical balance the mass could be determined to a tenth of a milligram, 60.5073 g. The beam balance is precise to the second place after the decimal, i.e., the numeral in the hundredths place represents the best estimate for that digit, indicating that the beaker weighs between 60.50 g to 60.52 g. The analytical balance has greater precision; the uncertainty in its measurements is the fourth place after the decimal. The two values for the mass of the beaker are differentiated by the number of **significant figures** in each quantity: 60.51 has **four** significant figures—three certain digits, **60.5**1 plus the uncertain digit, 60.5**1**. The second value, 60.5073, has **six** significant figures.

When recording data, it is important to indicate the proper number of significant figures in the measurement. If a crucible, weighed on an analytical balance, is found to have a mass of 21.0000 g, **all the zeros** after the decimal must be recorded to indicate the exactness of the measurement. If a student records "21 g" in his or her notebook, the actual precision of the measurement is lost. "21 g" indicates that the mass is 21 ± 1 g, not 21.0000 ± 0.0001 g actually measured on the analytical balance.

Be aware of the uncertainties associated with various pieces of equipment. The analytical and the multiple beam balances, described above, can be read to four and two places after the decimal, respectively. Burets may be read to hundredths of a mL. Volumetric glassware in general (graduated cylinders, pipets, etc.) can be read to one more decimal place than the smallest graduation, as illustrated in the following figure.

5.3 _____

_____ 5.25 (estimated)

5.2 _____

In reading "5.25" above, the first two digits are certain. The third is estimated and may vary from person to person.

Record all data to the proper number of significant figures. Retain all certain (always re-producible) numbers plus the first estimated number (may vary if the measurement is repeated).

Zeros introduce special problems into the determination of the number of significant figures in a numeral. Zeros preceding a number are **never** significant, while those that follow **may be**. The numeral 0.098 contains only two significant figures, since the zeros are used only to set the decimal point.

On the other hand, giving the population of Chicago as 3,607,000, does not necessarily mean that the population is known to the nearest person. This numeral has at least four significant figures, but there may be more. The problem is resolved by using **scientific notation**, writing the population as 3.6070×10^6, showing that the population is known to the nearest 100 people (five significant figures).

Zeros between other numerals are **always** significant. Thus 4.208 has four significant figures.

The number of significant figures in a measurement is important, since the uncertainty in a final answer is directly related to the uncertainties in the quantities used in the calculation. When numbers are multiplied or divided, the number of significant figures in the answer is the number of significant figures in the **LEAST PRECISE** number used in the calculation. This rule ensures that the relative uncertainty in the final result is about the same as the largest relative uncertainty in the numbers used to obtain the result. If one were to determine the volume of a box, measured the length and width very carefully as 1.310 m and 1.100 m, then hastily measured the depth as 0.5 m, it would be improper to express the volume to more than one significant figure. The imprecision in the third measurement destroyed the precision of the other two. The volume calculated would have to be rounded off to one significant figure:

$$1.310 \text{ m} \times 1.100 \text{ m} \times 0.5 \text{ m} = 0.7 \text{ m}^3$$

In adding and subtracting, one must pay attention to the absolute errors associated with the numbers to be added or subtracted. Adding 10.01 to 2.0031 properly gives the sum 12.01. A sum or difference cannot be expressed to more places after the decimal point than the term with the least number of places after the decimal point. In this example, 10.01 shows greater uncertainty (± 0.01) than does 2.0031 (± 0.0001), thus the answer is reported with only two places after the decimal point.

When the result of any arithmetic operation contains too many "significant" figures, the answer must be rounded off. Use the following rules:

1. If the last number to be rounded off is < 5, leave the preceding number the same.

2. If the last number to be rounded off is ≥ 5, raise the preceding number by 1.

To say that all measurements are uncertain does not mean that all **numbers** are uncertain. For example, a liter is defined to be exactly 0.001 cubic meter. Such a defined constant may be considered to have infinite certainty.

Error Analysis

To determine the accuracy of a measurement, one must know the magnitude of errors in the measurement. Errors may be classified as **systematic** or **random**. Systematic errors result from improperly calibrated instruments or improperly standardized chemicals. They are roughly the same throughout an experiment. For example, an improperly calibrated pipet might deliver 24.90 mL instead of 25.00 mL. Another example of a systematic error involves an improperly standardized reagent. If one uses NaOH that has been standardized and labeled 1.00 M, but is actually 0.98 M, this will introduce a systematic error into the experiment. Systematic errors affect what is called the **accuracy** of a measurement.

Random errors are scattered either way from a true value with equal probability. For example, in reading a buret, one may consistently read too high, leading to a systematic error as discussed above. However, when reading between the graduations on the buret, say at a volume of 24.38 mL, one might sometimes read it as 24.37 and sometimes as 24.39 mL. The random error, or **absolute uncertainty** of the buret reading is ±0.01 mL. In general, the absolute uncertainty of a reported measurement is understood to be ±1 unit in the last significant figure. The **relative uncertainty** of a measurement is the ratio of the absolute uncertainty to the measurement itself, expressed as a percent. In the above example, the relative error of the buret reading is (0.01 mL/24.38 mL) × 100 = 0.04%. Random errors affect the **precision**.

Suppose a student analyzes the percent of iron in a sample of iron ore and ends up with values of 23.45%, 23.48%, and 23.42%. These values are very **precise**, since they are so close together. However, if the true value is 42.80%, the results are not very **accurate**. A careless but lucky student may analyze the same sample and find the percentage of iron in the ore to be 25.28%, 34.92%, and 67.30%. The average is 42.50%, which is very accurate. However, this student's values are very imprecise.

The reliability of a measurement may be increased in several ways. The more duplicate measurements one makes, the more reliable the data. The answer is expressed as the average or arithmetic mean of all the trials. When making measurements, consistent use of laboratory instruments is vital; however, results that are clearly dubious may be discarded when calculating the average.

The **precision** of a series of measurements may be expressed in a number of ways. One of the most common is to find the **standard deviation**, the average of the differences between individual values and their average. For example:

result	1	65.69 g	deviation	1	0.14
	2	65.25 g	(difference from average)	2	0.30
	3	65.71 g		3	0.16
total		196.65 g	total deviation		0.60
average = 196.65/3 = 65.55			standard deviation = 0.60/3 = 0.20		

Note that the sign of the deviation is ignored to find standard deviation. (What would happen if the signs were included in finding the total deviation?)

The result is properly expressed as 65.55 ±0.20 g.

The **accuracy** of a series of measurements can only be determined if the correct answer is known independently of the experiment. Accuracy is expressed as a relative percent error:

$$\% \text{ error} = \frac{\left[\text{true result} - \text{experimental result}\right]}{\text{true results}} \times 100$$

Graphical Treatment of Scientific Data

Experimental data are often analyzed graphically. One of the variables, called the dependent variable, is plotted as a function of the other, called the independent variable. The form of the resulting graph shows the relationship between two or more variables. If these experimental variables, x and y, are directly proportional, the graph of this relationship is a straight line with the equation $y = mx$, where m is a constant, either positive or negative. Let us consider the Ideal Gas Law, $PV = nRT$, in an example. A plot of pressure, P, vs. temperature, T, of an ideal gas yields a straight line with slope m equal to nR / V, where R is the gas law constant whose numerical value depends on the units used for the measurements.

If $y = mx$, the value of y is zero when x is zero. However, two variables x and y may be directly proportional when x = zero, but y is equal to some constant, b. This type of relationship fits the equation $y = mx + b$.

A straight-line relationship of the form $y = mx + b$ is illustrated below. y is plotted on the vertical axis (the ordinate), and x on the horizontal (the abscissa). The value of b, the y-intercept, is found by locating the value of y when x is equal to zero:

$$y = (m\backslash 0) + b = b$$

The slope of the line, represented by the constant m, can be calculated by comparing any two points on the line:

$$y_1 = mx_1 + b$$

$$y_2 = mx_2 + b$$

Subtracting the first equation from the second gives:

$$y_2 - y_1 = m(x_2 - x_1) \text{ or } m = \frac{y_2 - y_1}{x_2 - x_1}$$

m is a measure of the rate of change in the value of y relative to the rate of change in the value of x. When $|m| > 1$, the value of y changes faster than that of x.

Another common relationship between two variables is that of **inverse proportionality**:

$$xy = k, \text{ or } y = \frac{k}{x}.$$

Again, let us use PV = nRT as an example. The pressure of an ideal gas is inversely proportional to its volume at constant temperature: PV = nRT or P = nRT / V. Plotting two inversely proportional variables will not result in a straight line. Such relationships will not be graphed in the laboratory exercises in this course because of the difficulty in fitting a curve to data points.

In many of the experiments in this course, you will plot data and evaluate constants from the slope and/or intercept of the resulting graph. The actual construction of graphs is a simple procedure, involving the following steps:

1. **Organize Your Data** in tabular form so that you have the values of the dependent variable adjacent to the values of the independent variable.

2. **Choose Appropriate Intervals** along the two axes so that data values are spread over as wide a range as possible.

3. **Label Each Axis** and give a title to the graph.

4. **Plot the Data Points**, making sure that they are clearly marked so that they will show up on the graph.

5. **Draw a Straight Line** that fits the plotted data points. (DO NOT connect the points by drawing a line from point-to-point.)

I

APPENDICES

Example:

The pressure of a certain quantity of gas in a container of fixed volume is measured at a series of temperatures. The data are organized as follows.

PRESSURE (TORR)	TEMP. (K)
33.0	305
36.2	310
39.5	315
43.0	320
46.0	325
49.2	330
52.4	335
55.6	340
58.8	345

The temperature is the independent variable and will be plotted along the horizontal axis; the pressure will be plotted along the vertical axis.

To calculate the slope, choose two random points, p_1 and p_2 on the line, with coordinates x_1, y_1 and x_2, y_2, respectively. Then, if $p_1 = (312, 37.5)$ and $p_2 = (337, 53.5)$:

$$m = \frac{y_2 - y_1}{x_2 - x_1} = \frac{53.5 - 37.5}{337 - 312} = 0.640 \text{ torr/K}$$

If the y-intercept cannot be read directly from the graph (as in this example), it can be calculated from the slope, m, and the x and y coordinates of any point on the line using p_2 again.

$$53.5 = 0.640\,(337) + b$$

$$b = -162$$

Thus, the equation for this line is:

$$y = 0.640x - 162$$

or

$$P = 0.640T - 162$$

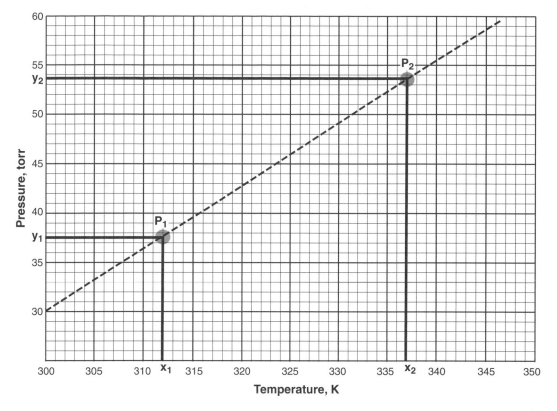

Pressure as a function of temperature

Exercises

1. Which number in each pair has a greater number of significant figures? If a pair of numbers has the same number of significant figures, indicate the number of significant figures.

   a. 6530, 0.006530

   b. 0.0010360, 0.000010360

2. How many significant figures are there in the following numbers?

   a. 0.000400

   b. 5805

   c. 7.00×10^4

   d. 170340.120

3. Convert the following to correct scientific notation.

   a. 0.00421300

   b. 100840

4. Perform the following arithmetical operations, giving the answer with the proper number of significant figures.

   a. $145.30 - 1.03 - 2.430$

   b. $4.32 \times 10^2 + 0.110 \times 10^4$

   c. $\dfrac{104369 \text{ g}}{4.6800 \text{ mL}}$

   d. $\dfrac{4.621 \times 0.00321}{98.010}$

   e. $\dfrac{12.032 - 9.0 + 27.02}{16.024}$

5. Using dimensional analysis, solve the following unit conversions. Show all your work, including units that cancel.

   a. $443 \text{ Å} = ? \text{ cm}$

   b. $11.21 \text{ g/mL} = ? \text{ lb/qt}$

6. Calculate the average and average deviation of the following set of measurements. Show your work.

42.10 mL	41.89 mL
41.98 mL	42.01 mL
42.34 mL	42.18 mL
42.25 mL	42.30 mL
41.60 mL	41.79 mL

   Average =

   Average deviation =

7. Assuming the true volume in question 6 is 42.10 mL, calculate the % error of the average value.

8. Define precision and accuracy. Which of the statistical values calculated above indicates the precision of the data set? The accuracy of the data set?

I

APPENDICES

Simple Laboratory Procedures

This appendix contains a discussion of some of the equipment you will use throughout the semester. You should become familiar with this material before beginning your laboratory work. Also, you should utilize the experience of your laboratory instructor or teaching assistant (TA) by calling on him or her to show you the best way to carry out any laboratory manipulation which you do not understand.

The Bunsen Burner

A convenient supply of heat in the laboratory is a simple Bunsen burner flame. In the Bunsen burner, air and gas are mixed in the barrel and ignited at the top. The amount of air which enters the barrel through holes in the base is regulated by a rotating sleeve at the bottom of the burner. The nature of the flame and the temperature are determined by the relative amount of air and gas admitted. The following procedures should be used always in lighting the burner.

1. **Close off** the air supply.

2. **Attach** the hose of the burner to the laboratory gas outlet and **turn on** the gas all the way.

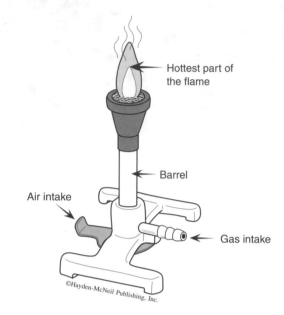

Hottest part of the flame

Barrel

Air intake

Gas intake

©Hayden-McNeil Publishing, Inc.

3. **Light** the burner by bringing a lighted match from the side to the top of the burner. Note the appearance of the flame.

4. **Open** the air inlet slowly and note that the flame becomes more colorless.

5. When the proper amounts of air and gas are entering, the flame should possess a bright blue cone with a surrounding area of darker blue. If this does not happen with the air inlet fully opened, decrease the amount of gas entering the flame until it has the proper appearance. The hottest part of the flame is the area just outside the inner blue cone.

   If a burner "flashes back" and begins to burn in the barrel, turn off the gas and let the burner cool before relighting it by the above procedure. Do not touch the barrel of the burner, which can get quite hot.

Measuring the Volume of Liquids

In the laboratory, various types of apparatus are used to measure volumes of liquids. Graduated cylinders, pipets, burets, and volumetric flasks are the most common. These can be calibrated either to contain or to deliver a specified volume. Volumetric equipment is marked by the manufacturer with either a **TD** (to deliver) or a **TC** (to contain). The temperature to which the calibration refers is also specified.

GRADUATED CYLINDERS
Graduated cylinders usually are calibrated to contain a specified volume, and thus are not suitable for the transfer of a volume of liquid from one container to another when a high degree of accuracy is required. For work in which high accuracy is not required, however, a graduated cylinder is a rapid means of transferring approximate volumes. Since water wets glass, the surface of the water forms a meniscus inside the cylinder.

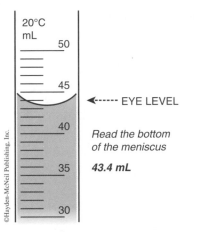

Figure AII-1. Volumetric glassware is calibrated using the bottom of the meniscus. In reading volumes, the eye must be at the same level as the meniscus or error due to parallax will arise. The correct reading for Figure AII-1 is 43.4 mL, the number to the right of the decimal point being estimated to ±0.1 mL.

PIPETS

Pipets are designed for the transfer of known volumes of liquid from one container to another. Most pipets are calibrated to deliver (TD). Volumetric pipets are calibrated to deliver one fixed volume, while graduated pipets are calibrated to deliver any volume up to the maximum capacity. If the pipet is to be used, the instructor will demonstrate the proper technique.

BURETS

Burets, like graduated pipets, allow the delivery of any volume up to the maximum capacity burets are calibrated to deliver.

A buret consists of a calibrated tube containing the liquid and some kind of valve by which the flow of liquid through the tip can be controlled. Most burets use glass or plastic stopcocks to control the liquid flow. Most laboratory burets are marked every 0.1 mL and volumes may be estimated to ±0.01 mL.

Cleaning

The buret should always be cleaned thoroughly before use with detergent and a long brush. After rinsing with water, a clean buret should flow uniformly with no water breaks. The appearance of water breaks is a sure indication of an unclean surface.

Filling

After cleaning, the buret must be filled with the appropriate solution. In order to avoid dilution of the solution with the water remaining in the buret after rinsing, the following procedure should be followed:

1. Add 5–10 mL of the solution and carefully rotate the buret to wet the walls completely.

2. Drain the liquid through the tip.

3. Repeat the above procedure twice.

The buret is now ready to be filled with solution. Fill it well above the zero mark. Free the tip of air bubbles by rapidly letting small quantities of liquid flow through the tip. Finally, lower the level of the liquid to the zero mark or below it, and take the initial volume reading.

Titration

The most common use of the buret is in titrations. Titration is a process of adding a measured volume of one solution to another until chemically equivalent quantities have been mixed. The point at which chemically equivalent quantities have been mixed is called the equivalence point or the stoichiometric endpoint. The endpoint of a titration may be determined by observing a physical change (usually color) in a material called an indicator. An indicator is a substance that changes color at or very near the equivalence point. The tip of the buret is placed well within the titration vessel (usually an Erlenmeyer flask). Initially the titrant is added from the buret in increments of a milliliter or so. The sample should be swirled constantly to obtain complete mixing. As the titration progresses, the increments added should become smaller until near the endpoint only a drop at a time is being added.

Very close to the endpoint, the walls of the vessel should be rinsed down with water before the titration is completed.

Figure AII-2. Arrangement in a titration.

Volume increments less than a normal drop may be taken by allowing a small volume of liquid to form on the buret tip and then touching the tip to the wall of the flask. This droplet is then combined with the bulk of the solution by rinsing with water from a wash bottle. At the endpoint, the final reading of the buret is taken and the initial read-

II

ing is subtracted from it to give the volume of titrant added. A convenient set-up for a titration is shown in **Figure AII-2**.

To aid in reading a buret, make a buret reader from a white card or a piece of paper. Draw a dark region with a clearly defined edge on the card. When reading the buret, place the card behind the buret so that the dark region is slightly below the level of the meniscus. This enhances the meniscus, making it easier to read. Volumes may be read to the nearest 0.01 mL.

VOLUMETRIC FLASKS

Volumetric flasks are calibrated to contain a specified volume. Various sizes are available, from 1 mL to several liters capacity. The most common uses of volumetric flasks are in the preparation of standard solutions and in the preparation of accurate dilute solutions from more concentrated standards.

To prepare a solution of known concentration by direct weighing, the desired amount of the solid is added to the volumetric flask by means of a funnel. The funnel is washed free of solid and the flask is filled about half full of solvent. After swirling to dissolve the solid, the flask is filled almost to the calibration mark. A wash bottle or dropper is used to bring the solution exactly to the mark. From the number of moles of solute added and the volume of the flask, the molar concentration of the solute may be calculated. For example, to prepare one liter of 0.1 M sodium chloride (formula weight = 58.44), exactly 5.844 g of NaCl are transferred to a 1 L volumetric flask and dissolved in water, then diluted to the calibration mark.

DILUTION OF REAGENTS

During the semester you will often need to prepare dilute solutions of acids and bases from concentrated stock solutions. Some examples of such dilutions follow.

Example 1:

Prepare 50.0 mL of 2.00 M HCl using 12.0 M HCl (conc. HCl) as the stock solution.

The final concentration is 1/6 the initial concentration. If 1 part of concentrated HCl is mixed with 5 parts of water, there will be 6 parts of solution. The acid will be 1/6 as concentrated as it was before, since the 1 part acid is mixed into 6 total parts. Thus:

$$(1)\left(\frac{50}{6}\right) = 8.3 \text{ mL of conc. HCl}$$

to be mixed with

$$(5)\left(\frac{50}{6}\right) = 41.7 \text{ mL of water}$$

II

APPENDICES

Example 2:

Prepare 10.0 mL of 1.0 M H_2SO_4 from concentrated (18.0 M) H_2SO_4.

Molarity times volume (M • V) equals the number of moles of solute. Since your final solution will have the same number of solute molecules as are in the quantity of concentrated acid you dilute, $M_1V_1 = M_2V_2$.

Here,

$M_1 = 18.0$ M $M_2 = 1.0$ M

$V_1 = X$ ml $V_2 = 10.0$ mL

$M_1V_1 = M_2V_2$

18.0 M $(X) = (1.0$ M$) (10.0$ mL$), X = 0.56$ mL

To about 9.0 mL of water, add 0.56 mL of concentrated H_2SO_4, then add water to the 10.0 mL mark. The resulting solution will be 1.0 M.

MOLARITIES OF COMMON CONCENTRATED REAGENTS		
Acetic acid	$HC_2H_3O_2$	17.5 M
Ammonium hydroxide	NH_4OH	15.0 M
Hydrochloric acid	HCl	12.0 M
Sulfuric acid	H_2SO_4	18.0 M
Nitric acid	HNO_3	15.8 M

Vacuum Filtration

This technique is used to separate a desired solid from a liquid. The apparatus is shown below. The Büchner funnel may be made of porcelain or polypropylene and its size should be appropriate to the collection flask.

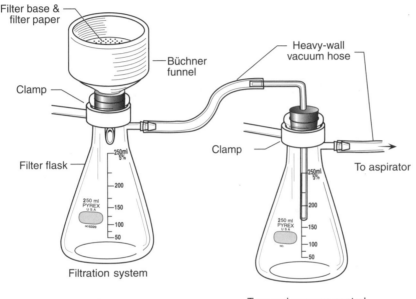

Filter base & filter paper

Büchner funnel

Heavy-wall vacuum hose

Clamp

Clamp

Filter flask

To aspirator

250 ml PYREX USA

250 ml PYREX USA

Filtration system

Trap and vacuum control

©Hayden-McNeil Publishing, Inc.

A trap may be omitted but is often useful in preventing any reverse suction, if an aspirator vacuum is used. It also prevents dirty solvent from being sucked into a central vacuum system, like that in your laboratory.

Moisten a piece of circular filter paper of the proper size with clean deionized water and place it in the funnel. Smooth it down so that it covers all of the holes. Pour the solution to be filtered slowly into the filter with most of the liquid going first leaving behind as much solid as possible. Finally, pour all of the solid onto the filter. Use a wash bottle filled with cold deionized water to transfer all the solid to the filter apparatus. When the mother liquor has been removed, wash the solid with some clean solvent that has been chilled a bit. The solid should also be broken up with a stirring rod to insure that all has been rinsed with clean solvent. The vacuum can be turned off when washing with this chilled solvent and then turned back on when ready to remove the solvent. Running the vacuum for a few minutes longer with air being sucked through will help to dry the solid.

You may notice some crystals of the solid forming in the filtrate below. This does not indicate a leaky filter. Rather, the vacuum causes cooling of the solution which results in some solid falling out of solution in the filter flask.

Check-In/Check-Out Information

Check-In Instructions

After you have turned in your breakage card, you will be assigned a locker. Open the drawer and inventory the contents using the check-in list on the following page. If you are unsure what a piece of equipment looks like, you will find diagrams on the following pages.

Inspect each item carefully. If any equipment is missing or broken, go to Room 206 Chem Annex for a replacement.

Be sure to put everything away at the end of each lab. Do **not** leave goggles or personal items in the drawer.

You are responsible for all equipment in your drawer. If equipment is lost or broken, you will have to pay for replacement materials. This fee will be deducted from your breakage fee card. Replacement equipment is purchased from the stockroom (206 Chem Annex).

> **SAFETY NOTE:** All broken glass must be placed in the designated containers on the center aisle. Your TA will show you the location of these containers. He or she will also outline procedures for disposing of broken glass.

Check-Out Instructions

1. Remove equipment from your drawer; put it on top of your bench.

2. Clean out your drawer; discard the old paper towels, old unknowns, disposable pipets, and other unusable material. Glass must be disposed of in the designated containers. **Do not throw away corks**. Place the corks on the cart located in the middle of the lab. Take the drawer out and tip it upside down. Sweep up whatever falls out. Replace the drawer. Be sure to remove any tape that is stuck to the drawer.

3. Lay new paper towels in the bottom of the drawer.

4. Sort the equipment. Dispose of unusable plastic items in the large trash cans.

5. KEEP **ONLY** THE ITEMS ON THE EQUIPMENT LIST. PAY ATTENTION TO THE **NUMBER** OF EACH ITEM YOU MUST HAVE. Put any items which do not appear on the list or any extra items on the excess equipment cart located in the middle of the lab.

6. Replace all missing or broken equipment; look at the excess equipment cart first to obtain missing equipment. DO NOT PILFER EQUIPMENT FROM OTHER DRAWERS. Obtain equipment from the stockroom (206 CA) **ONLY** IF IT IS NOT ON THE EXCESS EQUIPMENT CART.

7. Clean and rinse all glassware, spatulas, funnels, etc. Rinse out pipet bulbs well. Remove all tape from test tubes and other equipment. Discard tape in the trash cans.

8. Place all clean equipment back into the drawer in an organized fashion. Ask your TA to inspect your drawer, i.e., make sure every item on the equipment list is present and clean and the drawer is orderly and clean.

9. Take down all the equipment stored above the bench on the superstructure. If you find glassware, test tube racks, etc., place them on the excess equipment cart. Place any equipment which is so rusted that it cannot be used (e.g., clamps and rings on which the screws are frozen) in the garbage can.

10. Use a sponge and water to wipe off all equipment and hoses that were on the superstructure.

11. Use a sponge and water to wipe off the entire superstructure.

12. **In 1 and 201 CA**:

    A. The aisle, ring stands should be put back first. Next to the ring stands, place all rings. Group the remaining equipment on the superstructure. The order for the remaining equipment is: test tube holders and clamps, buret holders, wire gauze, clay triangles, miscellaneous equipment, and finally the rubber hoses.

    B. Get a brush and brush out the area inside your hood very well.

    C. Use a sponge and water to wipe off the hood, the entire bench top, and the drawer fronts.

    D. Pull out the trash cans underneath the sinks and use a broom to sweep out ALL the paper, broken glass, rubber bulbs, etc. If necessary, reach in to remove stray items or trash.

    E. Proceed to the end of your bench at the wall. Look along the wall, including behind the bench. Reach in and remove ALL the trash in this area. Return any usable equipment to the excess equipment cart.

    F. Use a sponge and water to wipe off all of the reagent stations located at the end of each bench.

    G. Use a sponge and water to wipe off the pipes above your work area. Wipe off all of the hoods and the entire bench top areas.

In 101 CA:

    A.   Place equipment back in the cupboards. Each cupboard should have:

        1 ringstand, 1 ring, 1 clamp, 1 burette holder, 1 Bunsen burner, and

        2 rubber hoses.

    B.   Clean out the hood area well.

    C.   Wipe off the hood, benchtop, and drawer fronts.

13. Inspect all the gas and vacuum outlets near your drawer. Especially check if vacuum outlets leak when closed. Hang a tag over any gas or vacuum outlets which do not work properly.

14. Clean the sink. First remove and thoroughly clean the rubber mat. Pick out and throw away all paper and tape attached to the mat. Next, completely remove and throw away all paper, tape, broken glass, boiling chips, etc. in the sinks. Be careful of the broken glass and dispose of it in the **designated** containers. Use a sponge and water to thoroughly scrub the sink. Rinse the sink with plenty of water. Finally, put the mat back into the sink.

Lab Equipment in Drawers Checklist

CHECK-IN LIST FOR RM. 1, 101 AND 201 CHEM ANNEX		CHECK IF PRESENT
Beakers	50 mL (1)	✓
	100 mL (4) (3)	✓
	150 mL (1)	✓
	250 mL (1)	✓
	400 mL (2)	✓
Erlenmeyer Flasks	50 mL (1)	✓
	125 mL (4)	✓
	250 mL or 300 mL (1)	✓
Test Tubes and Accessories		
	medium test tubes (6)	✓
	small test tubes (12)	✓
	large test tube rack (1)	✓
	small test tube rack (1)	✓
	small test tube brush (1)	✓
	large test tube brush (1)	✓
	test tube holder (1)	✓
Stir Rod with Rubber Policeman (2)		✓
Metal Spatula		✓
Plastic Wash Bottle		✓
Funnel		✓
Pair of Tongs		✓
Thermometer (−10°C – 100°C)		✓
Box of Matches		✓
Mohr Pipet (10 mL) (2)		✓
Pipet Bulb with Teflon Tip		✓
Sponge		✓
Wire Gauze		✓
100 mL/10 mL Graduated Cylinder (1) 10mL and (1) 100mL		✓
24 Well Trays (2)		✓

Lab Equipment

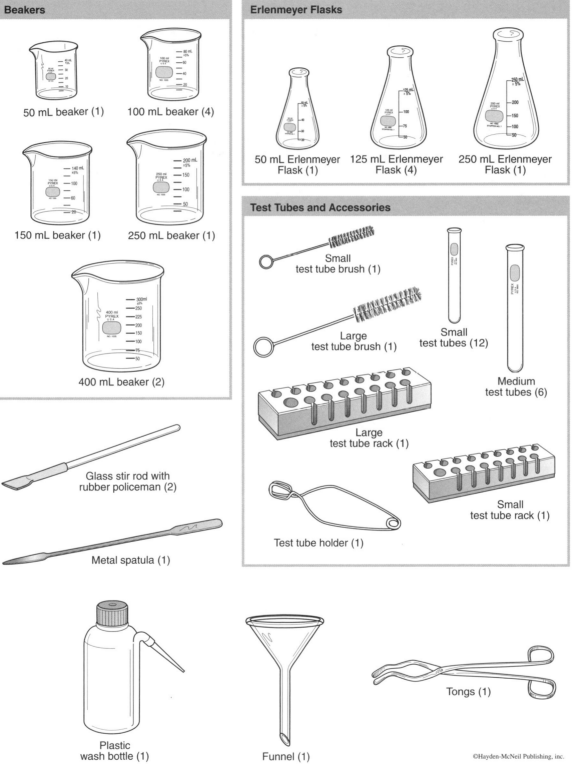

Beakers

50 mL beaker (1)

100 mL beaker (4)

150 mL beaker (1)

250 mL beaker (1)

400 mL beaker (2)

Glass stir rod with rubber policeman (2)

Metal spatula (1)

Plastic wash bottle (1)

Funnel (1)

Erlenmeyer Flasks

50 mL Erlenmeyer Flask (1)

125 mL Erlenmeyer Flask (4)

250 mL Erlenmeyer Flask (1)

Test Tubes and Accessories

Small test tube brush (1)

Large test tube brush (1)

Small test tubes (12)

Medium test tubes (6)

Large test tube rack (1)

Small test tube rack (1)

Test tube holder (1)

Tongs (1)

III

APPENDICES

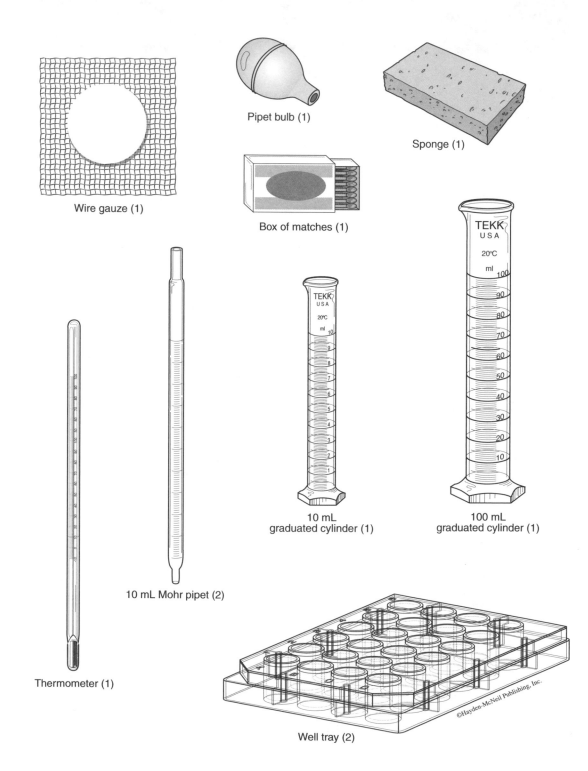

Wire gauze (1)

Pipet bulb (1)

Sponge (1)

Box of matches (1)

10 mL
graduated cylinder (1)

100 mL
graduated cylinder (1)

10 mL Mohr pipet (2)

Thermometer (1)

Well tray (2)

©Hayden-McNeil Publishing, Inc.

Frequently Asked Questions about Chemistry 103

1. **What do I need to have for Check-In?**

   You will need the Chemistry 103 Lab Manual, goggles, apron, and Breakage Fee Card (BFC). Come on the day and at the time listed on YOUR Section Schedule which is posted online. It takes about 45 minutes.

2. **What if I miss Check-In for my section?**

   Come prepared to do Experiment 1 at the first experiment lab period for your section, as listed on the Section Schedules. Contact the TA for your section if you have questions on what "prepared" means. The TA contact information is found on the "Contact Info" page of the Chem 103 website page.

3. **The Section Schedule lists an IVL or Post-Lab Quiz on a day and time I am scheduled to be in another class. What do I do?**

   Don't worry. The day and time listed is the DEADLINE. The computer will prevent you from doing the assignment afterward, but generally they are available for you to do for several weeks before the deadline.

4. **Is Chemistry 103 on the Web?**

   Yes. Chemistry 103 appears at: *www.chem.uiuc.edu*. Choose "Course Web Sites." Then choose "Chemistry 103". Surf the Chem 103 web page for more information.

5. **I cannot Log-in to Lon Capa. What should I do?**

   First, be sure you are using the correct login and password. Your login is your NetID and your password is your active directory password. Follow directions at *www.chem.uiuc.edu* for more help.

6. **Where can I find my lab grades?**

   All grades for lab are posted in the online gradebook which is regularly updated. Note: IVL grades are not posted to the online gradebook until the end of the term.

7. **I cannot logon to the IVLs. What do I do?**

Use your first name, last name and NetID to log in to the IVLs for the first time. You will be prompted to set your password the first time you log in. If you get a message that your name is not on the class roster see the Chem Learning Center supervisor who can create an account for you. The proctor sits at the front desk in the Learning Center in Rm. 212 Chem Annex.

8. **Is it useful to do the IVLs before we do the experiment on that subject?**

Absolutely. The IVLs will give you the basic concepts so that you can better understand the experiment. The IVLs don't take a long time to finish, but the benefits are priceless. If you take notes on the IVLs in your lab notebook, you can use them for the Post-Lab Quizzes.

9. **My IVL scores don't show up in the gradebook. What is going on?**

The IVL scores will be uploaded to the gradebook at the end of the semester. Chem-NET will give you an asterisk (*) for every lesson that you have finished. Make sure there is an asterisk by each of your completed lessons. If you are missing an asterisk, see the Chem Learning Center proctor, in Rm. 212 Chem Annex.

10. **Are there materials online that will help me prepare for each experiment?**

Yes! The "online laboratory syllabi" link on the website page for Chemistry 103 has a detailed procedure for each lab that incorporates color pictures and review questions. It is a good idea to print out these color pages and bring them with you to the lab. Also, the Lab Preview is designed to help you get prepared. You can take the lab preview quiz as many times as you like.

11. **How can I tell if and/or when I submitted an answer to each question?**

Once you have submitted a question on Lon Capa, a dialogue box that states "you have successfully submitted your question" should appear. If it does not, the question is not submitted and you should re-take the question.

12. **Are there make-up labs?**

No. There are no make-up labs in Chemistry 103. To be excused from a lab you must present a valid written excuse to your course director or your TA ASAP; no exceptions.

13. **Can I be excused from a lab?**

You must present a valid written excuse in order to be excused. Validity must be approved by the TA or by the course director. A second excused absence will require special circumstances and MUST be approved by the course director. More than two excused absences will result in failure of the Chemistry 103 course. Excused absences **DO NOT** excuse you from IVLs, Lab Previews, or Multiple Choice Post-Lab Quizzes.

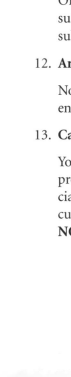

14. **What if my alarm did not go off in the morning, and I did not get to lab on time?**

This is not a valid excuse; it is your responsibility to attend all scheduled labs and exams. You will receive a grade of zero (0) for that lab.

15. **I have been attending the wrong lab section the whole semester. What should I do?**

First contact the course director to explain your situation. In most cases, it is easier if you keep attending the wrong section. The course director and TA will make the necessary arrangements for your grade to be reported to the University.

16. **Are significant figures important?**

YES, YES, YES. Significant figures are extremely important. The Chemistry 103 laboratory course is **strict** about significant figures. They will be accounted for in your Lab Reports and Lab Quizzes (see Appendix and Zumdahl text for details on significant figures).

17. **Are there any EXAMS for this course?**

No, not exactly. The "**EXAM**" for this course has been replaced with twelve computer-generated Post-Lab Quizzes.

18. **Can I take notes in my Lab notebook to use for the Post-Lab Quizzes?**

You are allowed to take notes from the IVLs in your notebook, and you are strongly encouraged to correct any lab report answers you had wrong on the yellow pages of your notebook.

19. **I am not sure of the answer to a Lab Preview or Post-Lab Quiz question. Can I get help?**

Yes, you are allowed to use **ANY** resource you need to help answer any question. Obviously, a Chem 103 TA, Lab Director or Learning Center Director are the best resources provided to help you correctly answer a question.

20. **I have submitted an answer to a Lab Preview or Post-Lab Quiz question. However, after talking to my TA and lab partner, I have decided I want to change my answer. Can I? How do I change my answer?**

You may change your answer as many times as you would like before the **DUE DATE** and **TIME**. The highest score of all attempts will be recorded in the gradebook.

21. **What if I miss a Lab Preview or a Post-Lab Quiz?**

You will not be allowed to make up any quizzes except in the case of prolonged illness or emergency. Last-minute computer problems do not suffice as reason to have a quiz deadline extended for you. If you miss a quiz due to illness or emergency, contact your TA and course director.

IV

APPENDICES

22. **My TA is a hard grader, but my friend's TA is an easy grader; can I change my section?**

No. If you have a hard grading TA, then stay with him/her until the end of the term. Changing sections will actually do you more harm than good because your grades will follow you and you will end up having a lower grade in your new section. The section scores will be normalized, so a tough grading TA will not hurt your overall grade.

23. **Will the lab course be curved?**

The lab report grades will be scaled to the class average and then verified against the scores of Post-lab Quizzes for each section. There is not an official curve for the course; for example, a score above 93% will be an A in the class.

24. **When will final grades be posted?**

The grades will be posted to the gradebook by the end of finals week.

25. **I think my grade is wrong. Who do I talk to?**

Sometimes problems arise; please notify the course director so that the problem can be corrected in a timely manner.

26. **I got a "W" grade for the course, but I went to all labs and completed all the computerized assignments. What do I do?**

Talk to the course director, **as soon as possible**. Don't let this mistake ruin your record. If you cannot locate the director, go to 107 CA and talk to one of the secretaries. If you let a long time go by, we won't be able to correct the problem.

27. **My Lon Capa assignment deadlines do not match my section schedule. What should I do?**

You were originally enrolled in a different section; your Lon Capa deadlines must be updated immediately. Email the course director with your full name, NetID and section.

28. **Do I have to complete the review questions in the "Experiments" link for a grade?**

No. These review questions are meant to help you prepare for your Lab Preview Quizzes and Post-Lab Quizzes.

AS CONDITIONS FOR USING THE LABORATORY IN THE STUDY OF CHEMISTRY 103, I WILL:

1. Wear safety goggles at all times. (Required by State Law.) Wear safety apron or lab coat at all times.

2. Never wear shorts, skirts, capris or open-toed shoes (especially sandals) to lab.

3. Read and understand the *Laboratory Conduct and Safety* information as outlined on pages xxi–xxii of this manual.

4. Know the location of all safety equipment—fire extinguishers, showers, eye washes and fire alarms—in the lab.

5. a. Dispose of all solid chemical waste in waste containers or special containers provided for special chemical wastes.

   b. Never throw solids (especially paper, matches, or glass) into the sink.

   c. Put all broken glass in the special containers designated by the TA and laboratory specialist.

6. Report any accident, broken equipment, or other damage **IMMEDIATELY** to the TA or the storeroom supervisor.

7. Clean up spills immediately.

8. Leave my work space and shared equipment ready for use by the next student to occupy the station.

9. Pay for any broken or lost equipment. The cost of items lost or broken will be deducted from my breakage fee card purchased as required material for Chemistry 103.

10. Have adequate insurance coverage to cover costs of transportation and treatment in the case of an emergency.

I have read and will follow all guidelines as stated above. I understand that failure to comply with these rules will adversely affect my laboratory grade and will be cause for dismissal from the lab.

_____   _____   _____
                Signature   Section   Date

_____
            Printed Name

CONDUCT
OF WORK

The Periodic Table

( ) = Estimates

Key:
- Symbol
- Atomic Number
- Atomic Weight
- Name

Example: H, 1, 1.008, Hydrogen

1 IA	2 IIA	3 IIIB	4 IVB	5 VB	6 VIB	7 VIIB	8	9 VIIIB	10	11 IB	12 IIB	13 IIIA	14 IVA	15 VA	16 VIA	17 VIIA	18 VIIIA
H 1 1.008 Hydrogen																	**He** 2 4.00 Helium
Li 3 6.94 Lithium	**Be** 4 9.01 Beryllium											**B** 5 10.81 Boron	**C** 6 12.01 Carbon	**N** 7 14.01 Nitrogen	**O** 8 16.00 Oxygen	**F** 9 19.00 Fluorine	**Ne** 10 20.18 Neon
Na 11 22.99 Sodium	**Mg** 12 24.31 Magnesium											**Al** 13 26.98 Aluminum	**Si** 14 28.09 Silicon	**P** 15 30.97 Phosphorus	**S** 16 32.07 Sulfur	**Cl** 17 35.45 Chlorine	**Ar** 18 39.95 Argon
K 19 39.10 Potassium	**Ca** 20 40.08 Calcium	**Sc** 21 44.96 Scandium	**Ti** 22 47.88 Titanium	**V** 23 50.94 Vanadium	**Cr** 24 52.00 Chromium	**Mn** 25 54.94 Manganese	**Fe** 26 55.85 Iron	**Co** 27 58.93 Cobalt	**Ni** 28 58.69 Nickel	**Cu** 29 63.55 Copper	**Zn** 30 65.39 Zinc	**Ga** 31 69.72 Gallium	**Ge** 32 72.61 Germanium	**As** 33 74.92 Arsenic	**Se** 34 78.96 Selenium	**Br** 35 79.90 Bromine	**Kr** 36 83.80 Krypton
Rb 37 85.47 Rubidium	**Sr** 38 87.62 Strontium	**Y** 39 88.91 Yttrium	**Zr** 40 91.22 Zirconium	**Nb** 41 92.91 Niobium	**Mo** 42 95.94 Molybdenum	**Tc** 43 (97.9) Technetium	**Ru** 44 101.07 Ruthenium	**Rh** 45 102.91 Rhodium	**Pd** 46 106.42 Palladium	**Ag** 47 107.87 Silver	**Cd** 48 112.41 Cadmium	**In** 49 114.82 Indium	**Sn** 50 118.71 Tin	**Sb** 51 121.76 Antimony	**Te** 52 127.60 Tellurium	**I** 53 126.90 Iodine	**Xe** 54 131.29 Xenon
Cs 55 132.91 Cesium	**Ba** 56 137.33 Barium	**La** 57 138.91 Lanthanum	**Hf** 72 178.49 Hafnium	**Ta** 73 180.95 Tantalum	**W** 74 183.85 Tungsten	**Re** 75 186.21 Rhenium	**Os** 76 190.2 Osmium	**Ir** 77 192.22 Iridium	**Pt** 78 195.08 Platinum	**Au** 79 196.97 Gold	**Hg** 80 200.59 Mercury	**Tl** 81 204.38 Thallium	**Pb** 82 207.2 Lead	**Bi** 83 208.98 Bismuth	**Po** 84 (209) Polonium	**At** 85 (210) Astatine	**Rn** 86 (222) Radon
Fr 87 223.02 Francium	**Ra** 88 226.03 Radium	**Ac** 89 227.03 Actinium	**Rf** 104 (261) Rutherfordium	**Db** 105 (262) Dubnium	**Sg** 106 (263) Seaborgium	**Bh** 107 (262) Bohrium	**Hs** 108 (265) Hassium	**Mt** 109 (266) Meitnerium	**Ds** 110 (271) Darmstadtium	**Rg** 111 (272) Roentgenium	Unnamed Discovery 112 (277)	Unnamed Discovery 114 (296)		Unnamed Discovery 116 (298)		Unnamed Discovery 118 (?)	

ALKALI METALS
ALKALI EARTH METALS
HALOGENS
NOBLE GASES

LANTHANIDES

Ce 58 140.12 Cerium	**Pr** 59 140.91 Praseodymium	**Nd** 60 144.24 Neodymium	**Pm** 61 (145) Promethium	**Sm** 62 150.36 Samarium	**Eu** 63 152.97 Europium	**Gd** 64 157.25 Gadolinium	**Tb** 65 158.93 Terbium	**Dy** 66 162.50 Dysprosium	**Ho** 67 164.93 Holmium	**Er** 68 167.26 Erbium	**Tm** 69 168.93 Thulium	**Yb** 70 173.04 Ytterbium	**Lu** 71 174.97 Lutetium

ACTINIDES

Th 90 232.04 Thorium	**Pa** 91 231.04 Protacinium	**U** 92 238.03 Uranium	**Np** 93 237.05 Neptunium	**Pu** 94 (240) Plutonium	**Am** 95 243.06 Americium	**Cm** 96 (247) Curium	**Bk** 97 (248) Berkelium	**Cf** 98 (251) Californium	**Es** 99 252.08 Einsteinium	**Fm** 100 257.10 Fermium	**Md** 101 (257) Mendelevium	**No** 102 259.10 Nobelium	**Lr** 103 262.11 Lawrencium

HAYDEN McNEIL

LAB REPORT
EVALUATION FORMS

NAME: _____   SECTION AND TA: _____

LAB PARTNERS: _____   DATE: _____

Title	( )
Introduction Comments:	( )
Procedure Comments:	( )
Data Comments:	( )
Observations Comments:	( )
Analysis Comments:	( )
Question #1 Comments	( )
Question #2 Comments:	( )
Deductions*	( )
TOTAL	**(30)**

* Points taken off for such things as unfinished pre-lab questions at the beginning of lab, missing or poorly prepared data tables, poor lab technique (not wearing goggles or lab apron, breaking glassware, spilling chemicals), etc.

NAME: _____   SECTION AND TA: _____

LAB PARTNERS: _____   DATE: _____

Title	( )
Introduction *Comments:*	( )
Procedure *Comments:*	( )
Data *Comments:*	( )
Observations *Comments:*	( )
Analysis *Comments:*	( )
Question #1 *Comments*	( )
Question #2 *Comments:*	( )
Deductions*	( )
TOTAL	**(30)**

* Points taken off for such things as unfinished pre-lab questions at the beginning of lab, missing or poorly prepared data tables, poor lab technique (not wearing goggles or lab apron, breaking glassware, spilling chemicals), etc.

NAME: _____   SECTION AND TA: _____

LAB PARTNERS: _____   DATE: _____

Title	( )
Introduction *Comments*:	( )
Procedure *Comments*:	( )
Data *Comments*:	( )
Observations *Comments*:	( )
Analysis *Comments*:	( )
Question #1 *Comments*	( )
Question #2 *Comments*:	( )
Question #3 *Comments*:	( )
Question #4 *Comments*:	( )
Deductions*	( )
TOTAL	**(30)**

* Points taken off for such things as unfinished pre-lab questions at the beginning of lab, missing or poorly prepared data tables, poor lab technique (not wearing goggles or lab apron, breaking glassware, spilling chemicals), etc.

NAME: _____   SECTION AND TA: _____

LAB PARTNERS: _____   DATE: _____

Title	
	( )
Introduction	
Comments:	( )
Procedure	
Comments:	( )
Data	
Comments:	( )
Observations	
Comments:	( )
Analysis	
Comments:	( )
Deductions*	
	( )
TOTAL	**(30)**

* Points taken off for such things as unfinished pre-lab questions at the beginning of lab, missing or poorly prepared data tables, poor lab technique (not wearing goggles or lab apron, breaking glassware, spilling chemicals), etc.

NAME: _____   SECTION AND TA: _____

LAB PARTNERS: _____   DATE: _____

Title	( )
Introduction *Comments:*	( )
Procedure *Comments:*	( )
Data *Comments:*	( )
Observations *Comments:*	( )
Analysis *Comments:*	( )
Question #1 *Comments*	( )
Question #2 *Comments:*	( )
Question #3 *Comments:*	( )
Question #4 *Comments:*	( )
Deductions*	( )
TOTAL	**(30)**

* Points taken off for such things as unfinished pre-lab questions at the beginning of lab, missing or poorly prepared data tables, poor lab technique (not wearing goggles or lab apron, breaking glassware, spilling chemicals), etc.

NAME: _____   SECTION AND TA: _____

LAB PARTNERS: _____   DATE: _____

Title	( )
Introduction	
Comments:	( )
Procedure	
Comments:	( )
Data	
Comments:	( )
Observations	
Comments:	( )
Analysis	
Comments:	( )
Question #1	
Comments	( )
Question #2	
Comments:	( )
Question #3	
Comments:	( )
Question #4	
Comments:	( )
Question #5	
Comments:	( )
Question #6	
Comments:	( )
Question #7	
Comments:	( )
Deductions*	( )
TOTAL	**(50)**

* Points taken off for such things as unfinished pre-lab questions at the beginning of lab, missing or poorly prepared data tables, poor lab technique (not wearing goggles or lab apron, breaking glassware, spilling chemicals), etc.